OVER THE HILLS

OF

MY BOOK HOUSE

EDITED BY

OLIVE BEAUPRÉ MILLER

PUBLISHERS

THE BOOK HOUSE for CHILDREN

LAKE BLUFF, ILLINOIS

PREFACE

IN "Over the Hills," the child, having passed through the gate, journeys still farther afield in his excursions into life. He travels to Switzerland in the beautiful story of "Heidi in the Alpine Pasture," written by the great Swiss author of children's stories, Johanna Spyri. In "The Nuremberg Stove," by Louise de la Ramée, he shares all the adventures of the boy August, hidden in the beautiful porcelain stove, and he goes with August on the thrilling journey from Austria to Munich.

In the matter of imaginative tales he also travels farther afield, for he is ready now to meet a few giants and monsters and share the bold adventures of the heroes who conquer them. By this time he unconsciously feels the fairy to be a great force for good, always appearing at just the right time to restore justice, to aid and protect virtue, to offer golden opportunities, and as unconsciously he feels the giants and monsters to be examples of evil, of cruelty, overbearance and bestiality, with whose overthrow and defeat, he heartily and rightly sympathizes. Thus in this volume he has among many other things, "Jack and the Beanstalk," "The Red Ettin," and "How Jack Sought the Golden Apples."

But at this period, as always, children should have stories in which the hero really has the true qualities of a hero with no mixture of the charlatan or imposter. After all, the folk tales from which our best fairy stories come, originated in the childhood of the race, expressing primitive emotions, primitive fancies, primitive fears and a primitive concept of good and evil. They were told first by adults to adults as a means of entertaining each other when they had no books to entertain them. So they were definitely not conceived for children and many of them are wholly unsuitable for children.

When the Grimm brothers went about Germany collecting from common people everywhere the stories their grandparents had told them because their grandparents had heard them from their grandparents, and so on, back through endless generations, these two brothers were gathering the tales to learn from them certain facts about the Germans and their development as a people. They did not in the first instance gather these tales for children although they have long been chiefly the property of children.

Thus these stories, like collections from many other countries, need intelligent sorting before they are given to boys and girls for whom they were never intended. It is from them that our best-loved, most vigorous, vital and beautiful fairy tales come, yet some of them contain elements that are very bad for children. There are, for example, those stories about parents who leave their children to die deserted in the woods—an idea that greatly upsets the child's basic sense of security, which rests on his utter faith that mothers and fathers always take care of their children. Then there would naturally be stories with twisted ethics and stories so gruesome as to be utterly horrifying. So the folk fairy tales given here and throughout My BOOK HOUSE have been chosen from those that have strength and beauty but are ethically sound and exciting without being overpoweringly, hauntingly gruesome.

In addition to such tales, this volume, appealing to the child's dawning interest in mechanics has a collection of engine stories, beginning with Jamie Watt and his discovery of the use of steam, on through the story of Fulton and the first steamboat. It also has the ridiculous story of "The Steamboat and the Locomotive," written by Gelett Burgess. There is also the ballad about Casey Jones, the brave engineer whose famous exploits made him another folk hero of the American people.

"Over the Hills" also includes stories that touch the highlights of American history. Beginning with two short poems about Columbus, this group covers the first Thanksgiving, the story of George Washington, a Fourth-of-July poem, and the story of Abraham Lincoln.

The poems about Columbus, including one by Annette Wynne, who thoroughly grasped the spirit of childhood, are animated presentations of the wisemen who pooh-poohed Columbus, telling him the world was flat and that he would meet dread monsters in the sea if he was foolish enough to sail beyond the known bounds of the world. These poems are exactly to the taste of children and they are illustrated not only with ridiculous pictures of the wisemen but also with pictures taken from an old illuminated manuscript showing the kind of monsters people of those days actually believed were in the distant unknown seas.

The story about Abraham Lincoln is preceded by a poem on Lincoln by one of our great modern poets, Stephen Vincent Benét, who wrote it in conjunction with his wife, Rosemary Benét. And as the function of poetry is to make one not only know and see but actually *feel* something, this poem makes the child not only see the tall gaunt man with a shawl around his shoulders but really *feel* his simple, kindly, warm humanity.

Following the story of Lincoln is another bit from our American folklore, the tale of the giant Negro, John Henry, the hero of the "steel-drivin'" men. Thus Volume Five completes Volume Four in presenting to children the best of our own American popular tales.

CONTENTS

The Story of Tom Thumb
AN ENGLISH FOLK TALE

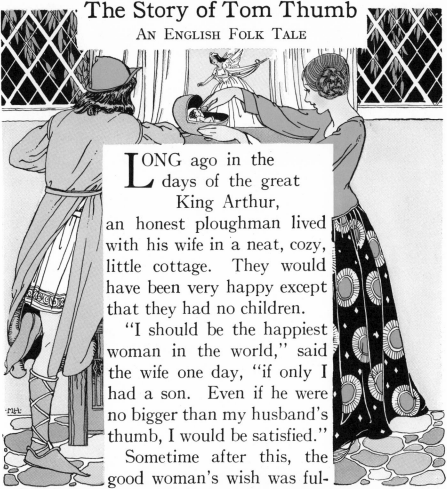

LONG ago in the days of the great King Arthur, an honest ploughman lived with his wife in a neat, cozy, little cottage. They would have been very happy except that they had no children.

"I should be the happiest woman in the world," said the wife one day, "if only I had a son. Even if he were no bigger than my husband's thumb, I would be satisfied."

Sometime after this, the good woman's wish was fulfilled. She did indeed have a son; and, strange to say, he was not one bit bigger than his father's thumb. The Queen of the Fairies, wishing to see the child, flew in at the window when he was but a few days old, and found his mother feeding him out of the cup of an acorn.

As soon as the Queen saw the little fellow, she kissed him and gave him the name of Tom Thumb. Then she sent for some of her fairies to come and dress him according to her orders. They made him a little hat of an oak leaf, his shirt was of spider's web, his jacket of thistledown, and his trousers of tiny feathers. His stockings were made of apple rind and his shoes of a mouse's skin.

Tom never grew any bigger than his father's thumb; but he was a brave, merry little fellow, so his parents loved 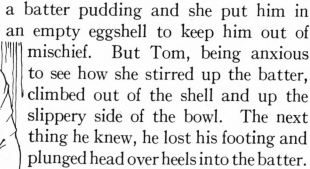 him dearly. One day his mother was making a batter pudding and she put him in an empty eggshell to keep him out of mischief. But Tom, being anxious to see how she stirred up the batter, climbed out of the shell and up the slippery side of the bowl. The next thing he knew, he lost his footing and plunged head over heels into the batter.

His mother never noticed him, but stirred him right into the pudding. Then she dumped him into the pudding bag and put him in the kettle to boil. The batter filled Tom's mouth and prevented him from crying out, but he kicked and struggled with all his might to get himself free. His mother, seeing her pudding dance madly around in the pot as if it were alive, seized it in alarm and threw it out the window.

Just then a tinker passed by; and, as he saw a nice-looking pudding coming his way, he picked it up and started to eat it. But Tom, having by that time freed his mouth of the batter, began to cry aloud: "Let me go! Let me go, Tom the Tinker!"

The Tinker was so startled to hear the pudding talk, that he flung it over the hedge and ran away as fast as his legs would carry him. But the fall had broken the pudding all to bits, so Tom crept out, all covered with batter, and made his way home. His mother was very sorry to see her darling in such a state, but she put him in a teacup and washed him off clean; then she kissed him and put him to bed.

Soon after this, Tom's mother went one day to milk her cow in the pasture and she took Tom along with her. It was a very windy day; and, in order to

13

make sure that Tom should not blow away, she tied him to a thistle with a strand of fine thread. The cow was peacefully eating; but she soon spied Tom's oak-leaf hat and, thinking it a choice morsel, she took up the little fellow and the thistle at a mouthful. When the cow began to chew, Tom had great difficulty to keep out of the way of her teeth and her tongue, but he called out boldly, "Mother! Mother!"

"My dear little Tommy, where are you?" cried his mother. "I'm here in the red cow's mouth!" Tom answered. At that, the cow, surprised at the odd tickling as of something moving in her throat, opened her mouth. Down her tongue slid Tom as on a toboggan slide. His mother caught him in her apron and ran off home at once.

OVER THE HILLS

Often Tom went to the fields with his father; and, as he was anxious to be of use, he one day begged to be allowed to take home the horse and cart.

"You! Why you couldn't even reach up to the top of the horse's hoofs!" laughed the father. "How do you think you are ever going to hold the reins?"

"Oh," answered Tom quite confidently, "I don't need to hold the reins. I'll just sit in the horse's ear and call out which way he is to go!"

The father was amazed to find his son so bold and clever, so he put Tom in the horse's ear and off he went.

"Yeo-hup! Yeo-hup!" cried Tom and he guided the horse so well, that he reached home in no time at all. Tom's mother was greatly surprised when she saw the horse arrive at the cottage with no one in sight as a driver; but Tom called out, "Mother! Mother, take me down! I'm in the horse's ear!"

"Now just to think of a little man like you driving a great big beast like that!" cried the mother and she was so pleased with what Tom had done, that she lifted him carefully down and gave him a whole big red currant for his supper.

Seeing how helpful his son could be, the father now made him a little whip of a barley straw, so he could sometimes drive the cattle home. As he was in the field thus at work one day, a raven spied him and picked him up—soaring high in the air and carrying him away. He dropped him, at last, from his talons into the top of a tree near a giant's castle. Pretty soon, out came the giant for a walk on the terrace. Mistaking Tom for the fruit of the tree, he plucked him off the branch and opened his mouth to swallow him. But just then along through the air came the Queen of the Fairies, in a chariot drawn by flying mice. Snatching Tom from the giant's hand, she placed him beside her and drove off to Fairyland.

In that lovely country Tom spent many happy days, being well-entertained by the fairies; but, after a time, the Queen dressed him in a new little suit of bright green, and sent him floating on a lively breeze straight to King Arthur's palace. As Tom was flying over the palace yard, the king's cook passed along below with a great bowl of the king's favorite dish, frumenty. At that moment the breeze dropped Tom and he fell plumb into the middle of the bowl, making the cook drop it with a smash and spill all the king's dainty frumenty.

"Help! Help! Thieves!" cried the cook who was a red-faced, coarse-grained fellow.

Swearing that Tom had meant to play this trick on him, the cook put Tom in a mousetrap, intending to keep him there till he could make complaint of him before the king.

But the cat, seeing something moving in the cage, thought Tom was a mouse; so she rolled the cage about between her paws till she broke it and set Tom loose. Then Tom ran off and hid in an empty snail's shell. There he stayed until he grew hungry. Peeping out in search of some means to get food, he saw a butterfly alight on a nearby flower; so he sprang at once astride the butterfly's back and the little creature flew with him up in the air, flitting from flower to flower. At last, attracted by a light in the king's dining-room, the butterfly flew in the window. King, queen, and nobles saw him and tried to catch him, but they could not. Nevertheless, with the butterfly's darting to keep out of reach, Tom—having neither saddle nor bridle—lost his seat on the butterfly's back and fell sprawling on the table.

King, queen, and nobles all spied the little man at once, and everyone was delighted with him. Far from punishing him for spoiling his frumenty, the king gave him half a blackberry for his supper, and he soon became a great favorite. His tricks and gambols and lively words amused the whole court; and, when the king rode out, he often took Tom along, he thought so much of his company. If it happened to rain, Tom would creep in the king's pocket and sleep there quite cozily till the rain was over.

At length King Arthur ordered a little chair to be made, so that Tom might sit before him on the table. And he also caused to be built for Tom a palace of gold, with a door just an inch in width, and he gave him a little golden coach with six white mice to draw it.

But Tom still thought of his mother and father; and, one day, he asked the king to let him pay them a visit. King Arthur not only consented, but, when he heard that Tom's parents were poor, he led him to the treasury where he kept all his gold and told him he might take home as much money as he could carry. With difficulty Tom dragged out a three-penny piece, and loaded it on his back. Then he toiled along the road for two days beneath his burden before he reached his father's cottage.

Tom's mother met him at the door and she could not thank him enough for having taken so much trouble as to drag home a three-penny piece, all for love of his father and mother. She placed him in a cozy walnut shell beside the fire; and she feasted him for three days, until he had consumed the whole of a hazelnut. When he had thoroughly rested, his duty told him the time had come for him to return to court. So he said good-bye to his mother and father and set off on his way.

As soon as he reached the castle, King Arthur made him a knight. Sir Thomas Thumb he was now called, and the king gave him a needle for a sword and a mouse for a horse. Thus armed and thus mounted, Tom rode with the king and his knights, and all enjoyed a hearty laugh at sight of Sir Thomas and his prancing steed. One day as they passed a farmhouse, a big black cat jumped out and rushed on Tom and his mouse. But Tom drew his needle at once and so boldly defended himself that he kept the cat at needle's length till one of the king's knights came and carried him safely home.

Thus Sir Thomas Thumb held his own in the world very bravely and was withal so merry, that he won the affection of all. In later years he often sang:

"My name is Tom Thumb;
From the fairies I've come;
When King Arthur shone,
His court was my home.
In me he delighted,
By him I was knighted.
Did you never once hear
Of Sir Thomas Thumb?"

Jack and the Beanstalk*
AN ENGLISH FOLK TALE

ONCE a poor woman lived in a hut with her only daughter and her only son, Jack. Years before, the woman had had a good house and lived in plenty, for her husband had been a harper, who wandered about, collecting money by playing his harp for people. But one day he had been on a forest path, coming home after playing in a great lord's castle, when he had suddenly disappeared. Many people said he must have been carried off by someone who wanted his magic golden harp. But nobody actually knew what had become of him. So Jack and his mother and sister, left with no breadwinner in the family, had grown poorer and poorer. Now they had nothing left but one cow which was at the moment giving no milk. So the mother said sadly one day:

*Save for the picture above, the illustrations for this story were made by the famous English illustrator George Cruikshank, who died in 1878 and is best known as the illustrator of all the works of Charles Dickens.

"Jack, you'll have to go to market and sell our poor Bossy or we'll have nothing to eat."

"Trust me!" Jack swaggered. "I'll sell her! And for a good price!" Then off he went with Bossy, sure he was smart enough to drive a shrewd bargain with any buyer.

At the market a funny old man came toward him.

"I see you have a cow for sale!" he said.

"Aye!" Jack answered. "A cow worth plenty of money!"

"Well, you look a proper sort of chap to sell cows!" the old man went on. "I wonder if you know how many beans make five!"

"Why, two beans in each of your two hands and one in your mouth—that will make five!" Jack felt very clever at answering that question so quickly.

"Right!" said the man. "And here they are, the very beans themselves!" Then he pulled some red and blue beans from his pocket. "You're surely a smart young fellow! So I offer you these beans in exchange for your cow!"

"Go along!" said Jack. "Beans won't buy a cow!"

"Ah! But you don't know what these beans are!" said the man. "They're magic beans! They'll perform wonders!"

"Really? You don't say!" Jack eyed the bright colored beans with increasing interest. Who knew what wonders he might work with magic beans? Almost before he knew it, Jack had accepted the beans and turned Bossy's halter over to the man. Then he hurried home.

"Back already, Jack?" said his mother. "Well, son, how much did you get for Bossy?"

"A lot! You'll never guess how much!" Jack boasted.

"Maybe you got ten pounds?" the mother queried.

"I said you couldn't guess! Look!" Jack opened his hand and showed the beans. "I got all these magic beans!"

"What!" Jack's mother was ready to weep. "For a few bright colored beans you've sold our Bossy! Now we'll have nothing to eat for supper nor for all the days to come!" Angrily taking the beans from his hand, she threw them out the window. "Tonight you'll have to go to bed hungry just as your sister and I will!"

So Jack, mightily taken down, went to his little room. Sad and sorry he was, more for the sake of his mother and sister than for the loss of his supper. But above all he was ashamed because he began to suspect that he hadn't really been very clever in selling Bossy for a few beans.

When he got up next morning, the sun was shining. But he still felt sad as he went to look out the window. Then all at once he saw a most marvelous sight. For the beans which his mother had thrown away the night before had now sprung up into a big tall beanstalk that went up and up and up till it was out of sight in the sky!

At once that beanstalk gave Jack an idea. Maybe he hadn't done so well in selling Bossy the day before but this beanstalk was surely magic! Who knew what chance of wondrous adventure might lie beyond it! Maybe up there he'd find treasures to make up to his mother for the disappointment he'd caused her. Opening his window he jumped out and started to climb the beanstalk.

Up he climbed, up he climbed, up he climbed! Through
a layer of clouds he went and still on up toward the sky—
up and up and up! By-and-by he saw that the beanstalk
ended at the edge of a rocky cliff which hung on nothing.

23

But Jack stepped out on the rock and there he saw a long broad road going off straight before him. So he walked along and he walked along till he came to a big tall house, where a big tall woman stood on the doorstep.

"Good morning, mum!" Jack said very politely. "Could you be so kind as to give me some breakfast?"

"So it's breakfast you want!" said the big tall woman. "Well, it's breakfast you'll *be* if you don't run off in a hurry! My man's a giant, and there's nothing he'd like better than a boy broiled on toast for his breakfast! So take yourself off! He may be home any moment!"

"Oh, please mum, do give me something to eat!" Jack pleaded. For having had no supper the night before, he was as hungry as a bear.

Well, the giant's wife wasn't so bad as she looked. Taking Jack into the kitchen, she gave him a hunk of bread and a piece of cheese. But Jack had scarcely started to eat when thump! thump! thump! the whole house began to tremble with the noise of someone coming.

"Good gracious! It's my old man," said the giant's wife. "Quick, you! Jump in here!" And she bundled Jack into the oven just as the giant came blustering in.

Sniffing about him, the giant shouted, "Wife, what's this I smell?" Then he roared like thunder:

> "*Fee-fi-fo-fum!*
> *I smell the blood of an Englishman!*
> *Be he alive, or be he dead,*
> *I'll have his bones to make my bread!*"

"Nonsense, dear!" said his wife. "You're dreaming! I've three whole oxen broiling for your breakfast! That's what you smell! Now you just go and have a wash and tidy up! By that time you can sit down to eat!"

Then off the giant went. Jack was about to jump out of the oven and run away when the woman told him to wait until her husband went to sleep, as he always did, after he ate. So Jack stayed in the oven while the giant came back and ate his breakfast. After that the woman went off with a pail to get water.

Then the giant took some money bags from a chest. Sitting down at the table again, he began to count the coins, chuckling and babbling to himself about the different people from whom he'd stolen the money. And as he poured out the coins from one bag he began to babble and boast about how clever he'd been in seizing a harper on a forest path together with his money and his magic golden harp.

At that Jack pricked up his ears. A harper seized on a forest path! That could only have been his father! And that bag of money! It had been stolen from his father! By this time the giant was sleepy. Soon his head began to nod and he started to snore so the whole house shook. Then before you could say Jack Robinson, Jack crept out of the oven, slipped past the giant, seized his father's money bag and raced back to the beanstalk. Down he climbed and down until at last he got home.

Proudly he told his mother and sister all that had happened and his mother was more than glad to have that sorely needed money. But the first thing she said was:

"Jack! Your father! Maybe he's still alive! Maybe the giant is holding him a prisoner up beyond the beanstalk!"

"Now why didn't I think of that?" Jack cried. And he felt ashamed of himself. So he decided to climb the beanstalk again and have a look around for his father.

Up he went the very next day and there on the doorstep of the big tall house stood the big tall woman as before.

"Good morning, mum!" said Jack. "Could you be so good as to give me something to eat?"

"You!" cried the big tall woman. "Aren't you the boy who came here before? Aye! And on that very day, my man missed one of his money bags! What do you know about that?"

"Well, I dare say I could tell you something about it!" Jack answered. "But right now I'm so hungry I can't speak! I can't tell you what I know until I've had something to eat!"

So the big tall woman, being very curious to learn what had happened to that money, took him in and gave him some bread. But he had scarcely begun to eat when thump! thump! thump! they heard the giant's footstep, and his wife hid Jack in the oven again.

All happened as it had before. In came the giant and had his breakfast. Then he said: "Wife, bring me the hen that lays the golden eggs." So she brought him a little brown hen. Then off she went with her pail.

When she had gone the giant said, "Lay!" to the hen. And the hen laid an egg of gold. This the giant did again and again until he got tired of his fun. Then his head began to nod and he started to snore till the house shook.

At that Jack crept out of the oven. Without giving the matter a second thought, he seized the hen and was off. But the hen began to cackle loudly and the noise she made awakened the giant. Thinking his wife had taken his hen, he started to bawl:

"Wife, wife, what are you doing with my golden hen?"

So with the giant awake, Jack had no time to look around for his father. He had to rush to the beanstalk. Down he climbed like a house afire.

When he got home he showed his mother and sister the wonderful hen and said, "Lay!" to it and it laid a golden egg every time he said, "Lay!"

But though his mother and sister were pleased with the hen, the first thing his mother said was:

"Jack! Oh, Jack! Did you see any signs of your father up there beyond the beanstalk?"

Then Jack was sorry again because he'd rushed off with the hen and lost his chance to search for his father. Well, he didn't let the grass grow under his feet before he set out to remedy his mistake. The next day he climbed the beanstalk a third time. But now he did not go straight to the giant's house. When he got near it he hid behind a bush until he saw the giant's wife come out with her pail to get water. Then he crept into the house and spying a big black kettle beside the hearth, he jumped into it swiftly, letting the lid down after him.

He hadn't been there long when again he heard thump! thump! thump! and in came both the giant and his wife. Sniffing about him, the giant roared more fiercely than before:

"Fee-fi-fo-fum! I smell the blood of an Englishman! I smell him, wife! I tell you, I smell him!"

"Do you now, dearie?" said the giant's wife. "Well, if it's that little rascal that made off with the money and the hen that laid the golden eggs he's sure to be hidden in the oven."

Then they both rushed to the oven. But Jack wasn't there! And the giant's wife cried to the giant:

"There you go making mistakes again with your big fee-fi-fo-fum! I'm tired of your fee-fi-fo-fums! Sit ye down and eat your breakfast!"

So the giant sat down and ate, but every now and then he muttered, "Well, I could have sworn—" And he got up and searched the larder and the cupboards and everything, only, luckily, he didn't think of the kettle.

At last when he'd finished eating he cried, "Wife, bring me my golden harp!"

And when Jack heard the word harp his heart beat fast. Lifting the lid of the kettle a little, he peeped out into the kitchen. Soon the woman brought the harp, set it on the floor before her husband and left him with it. And sure enough, Jack saw it was his father's harp. A beautiful thing it was—all carved of gold. And on the front was the figure of a woman with wings.

"Sing!" the giant commanded and with no one touching the strings, the harp gave forth beautiful music until the giant fell asleep again.

Then Jack slipped very quietly out of the kettle. But no sooner was he on the floor than the harp cried, "Master! Master!" And spreading its wings it started to fly out the door, like a bird scuttling over the ground.

At once Jack darted after it and it led him down steps and steps and through little dark passageways until he came to the dungeons in the cellar. And there it led him to a door, through the barred openings of which he could see a bearded man, lying drearily, very drearily, on a dirty bed of straw.

"Master! Master!" the harp twanged again. At that the man sprang up calling out, "My harp!"

But Jack cried, "Father, Father!"

Then the man saw him and said, "My son! Oh, my son! Art thou come to save me?"

"Aye, Father, aye!" Jack answered. And with that he ran to a little room near the dungeons where he found on a huge iron ring the keys to his father's prison. Returning, he unlocked the door and set his father free. Then after a quick embrace, the two set out with the harp.

But by this time the giant was awake. As they passed the kitchen door he saw them, gave a terrible roar and came plunging after them.

"Jump on the harp!" Jack's father cried.

So they both jumped on the harp. It spread its wings and flew off toward the cliff.

Roaring furiously, the giant chased them on, on, on, to the very edge of the cliff.

There, in his rage, he threw stones at them. Then for the
first time he noticed the beanstalk, and started to climb
down after them. But the harp got the two home safely.
Jack's mother and sister were greeting his father with tears
of joy when, lo and behold, what did all four of them see?

They saw the giant almost on them! But Jack got an axe
and chopped the beanstalk in two. So the giant fell down
and broke his crown and the beanstalk came tumbling
after! Bang, bang, smash! That was the end of the giant!

Dick Whittington and His Cat

AN ENGLISH LEGEND

ALONG time ago, in the reign of King Edward III, there lived in England a boy called Dick Whittington. Dick had no father or mother and he was very poor. Often he had nothing to eat and he was happy, indeed, when the poor people in the village could spare him a crust of bread or a few potatoes.

Now, these good country folk forever talked about London. Not one of them had really been there, but they seemed to know all about it just the same. Some said that all the people who lived in London were fine gentlemen and ladies, and that there was singing and music there all day long. Others said that nobody was ever hungry there, and the streets were all paved with gold.

Dick listened eagerly to these stories, and began to wish with all his heart that he could visit that wonderful city. One day, there came dashing up to the village inn a great wagon drawn by eight horses — all with bells on their heads. Dick said to himself, at once, that this wagon must be going to the fine city of London.

When the driver was ready to start off again, the lad ran up to him and asked if he might not walk by the side of the wagon. Thinking that such a ragged boy could not be worse off than he was at present, the driver told him that he might do as he liked. So off started Dick with the wagon. It was a long walk for a boy, but Dick trudged sturdily on until at last he came to the great, big city of London. In such a hurry was he to see the wonderful sights that he ran off as soon as he got there, forgetting altogether to thank the good-natured driver. Up one street and down another he went, trying to find those marvelous streets that were paved with gold.

"Now," he thought to himself, "if I could only find those golden streets, I could break a little bit off the pavement and buy everything I need."

He ran and ran and ran till he was so tired he could go no farther, but in all the streets there was only dirt and not a sign of gold. At last, as night was falling, he sat down in a dark corner and cried himself to sleep. When he awoke, it was morning, and he was very hungry. Having nothing whatever to eat and no money with which to buy food, he walked from one street to another, begging for just a penny from the people whom he met.

"Go to work, you idle fellow," cried some of these; and the rest passed him by without even looking at him.

By and by, having grown so hungry and tired he could go no farther, he lay down by the door of a very fine house.

"If only I knew how to find work!" he sobbed.

OVER THE HILLS

"What are you doing there, you little beggar?" It was the cook of the house calling to him. "Get away quick, or I'll throw my panful of dishwater over you! It's hot enough to make you jump!"

But just at that moment, the master of the house, a man named Mr. Fitzwarren, happened to be coming home to dinner. When he saw the ragged little fellow lying so forlorn at his door, he said to him very kindly:

"Well, well, my lad! Why are you lying there? You seem old enough to work. Can it be you are lazy?"

"No, indeed!" cried Dick. "I'd work with all my heart, if I could find anything to do. But I don't know a soul in London, and I haven't eaten for so long!"

"Poor little fellow!" said Mr. Fitzwarren. "Come into the house and I'll see what I can do for you."

So the merchant took the lad into his home. He ordered the cook to give him some dinner and then find him some sort of work. Thus it was that Dick was well-settled in the Fitzwarren house where he would have lived very happily, if it had not been for the cook.

"You are under my orders now!" she would cry. "Stand around there! Clean the spit! Make the fires! Wash these dishes! Bring in the wood! And do it all quickly or . . ." And she would shake her ladle, box his ears, or flourish her broomstick over his shoulders.

At last, however, little Mistress Alice Fitzwarren, daughter of the merchant, chanced to see how the lad was treated and she told the cook she would be turned

away at once if she did not use him more kindly. After that, Dick had an easier time; but there was still something else that troubled him.

His bed was in a garret at the top of the house, and there were so many holes in the floor and walls that, every night, great numbers of rats and mice came in. They raced back and forth over Dick, and made his room so unpleasant that he did not know what to do. One day he earned a penny from a gentleman for cleaning his shoes, and he said to himself that the best use he could make of the money would be to buy a cat with it. The very next morning he met a girl with a cat in her arms.

"I'll give you a penny for that cat," he said.

"Well and good!" the girl answered. "You may have her, and you'll find mice don't stay where she is."

So Dick hid his cat in the garret, and, every day, he was careful to save a part of his dinner and carry it up to her. Soon she had driven all the rats and mice away, so Dick slept soundly every night.

Not long after this, a ship that belonged to Mr. Fitzwarren was loaded and made ready to start on a voyage to a far-off land across the sea. Now, Mr. Fitzwarren always gave his servants the chance to send out in his ships something of their own, in the hopes of trading it at a good profit for them; so he called his servants together and asked what each would like to venture on this vessel. Everyone had something to send—everyone, that is, but Dick. As he had neither money nor goods, he did not join the servants in the parlor. Little Mistress Alice guessed at once why he did not come.

"Father," she said, "surely Dick should have a chance with the others. Here is some money from my own purse that you may take for him."

But Mr. Fitzwarren answered, "No, my child! He must send something of his own." Then he called Dick and said, "What are you going to venture on the ship, my lad?"

"I have nothing in the world to send," answered Dick, "nothing, but a cat."

"If you have a cat, fetch her and let her go," said Mr. Fitzwarren. "Who knows but that she may be traded for some good profit to you!"

So Dick brought poor Puss with tears in his eyes.

He carried her to the ship himself and gave her to the Captain with many farewell squeezes. Everybody laughed at the thought of making a fortune by trading nothing but a cat—everybody, that is, except Mistress Alice, and she was sorry for Dick and tried to comfort him.

After that, though Dick worked as faithfully as ever, the cook grew more and more ill-tempered. She made fun of him, too, for sending his cat to sea.

"Perhaps your puss," she would say, "will sell for money enough to buy a stick to beat you!"

At last Dick could no longer bear the hard work and the harsh treatment; so he made up his mind to leave the place. He packed up his few poor belongings and very, very early on All-hallows Day, he started away from the house. He walked as far as Holloway, and there he sat down to rest for a moment on a stone.

But as he sat there, sadly wondering which road he should take, he suddenly heard the six great bells on Bow Church in the distance, ringing out a merry chime. What was it they seemed to say? How strange! What was it they said? That distant chime seemed to say:

"Turn again, Whittington,
Thrice Lord Mayor of London!
Turn again, Whittington,
Thrice Lord Mayor of London!"

"Lord Mayor of London!" cried Dick. "Could I be Lord Mayor of London? If I thought I could, that would be worth working for! 'Turn again,' the bells said. Yes, that's just what I'll do. I'll turn back to my work. Let the old cook cuff and scold me as she pleases! I've got something to work for! To be Lord Mayor of London!"

And Dick went back to his work as quickly as he could. Happily, he reached the kitchen and was already at work before the cook came downstairs. And the stone on which he sat and made that important decision is to this very day called "Whittington's Stone."

Meantime Mistress Puss was journeying over the sea in Mr. Fitzwarren's ship. The ship made a very long voyage; and, at last, it was driven by the winds up on the coast of Africa. The Moors, who lived in those parts had never seen white men before, and they came in great crowds to stare at the pale faces of the strangers. Soon they were buying the fine things with which the ship was loaded. Seeing this, the Captain sent samples of his best wares to the king of the country, which was Barbary. It was not long after this before the king sent for the Captain to come and visit the palace.

As soon as the Captain arrived, he was shown at once into a splendid chamber and invited to seat himself on a rich and beautiful carpet all flowered with silver and gold.

The King and Queen sat in state at the upper end of the room, and no sooner was all in readiness than a number of servants came in bearing steaming dishes of food. But scarcely had they set the dishes down upon the table, when an army of rats and mice rushed pellmell into the room and devoured all the food in a twinkling. The Captain wondered greatly. "Is it not most unpleasant," he asked, "to have so many rats and mice about the palace? And do you do nothing at all to drive them away?"

"Alas!" the King answered. "It is, indeed, most unpleasant, but we have tried in vain to drive the mice and rats away. I would give half my treasure to be rid of them."

At that an idea flashed suddenly into the Captain's mind! Dick Whittington's cat! The Captain cried out to the King that he had a little creature on his ship which would make short work of the pests.

The King was overjoyed. "Bring her here to me," he said. "If she will do what you say, I will load your ship with gold in exchange for such a treasure!"

"I do not like to part with her, but to oblige your Majesty, I will fetch her," said the Captain.

"Do! Ah, do!" cried the Queen.

So the Captain went down to the ship, while another dinner was being made ready in the palace. He took Puss in his arms and returned to the King, just in time to see a second army of rats rush out on the newly-brought food. Seeing those rats and mice, Puss was out of the Captain's arms and in among her foes in an instant. How she made

after the creatures! And how they scampered away! Soon there was not one single mouse or rat left on the table!

The King cried out in his joy, and the Queen desired that the pretty little creature which had served them all so well, should be brought for her to look at. "Pussy, pussy, pussy!" called the Captain, and Mistress Puss came bounding in a very graceful way. The Captain lifted her up to put her on the Queen's lap, but the Queen drew back at first and was half-afraid to touch her. But when she saw how the Captain stroked the pretty, soft fur, and called "Pussy, pussy, pussy!" she ventured to stroke her, too. "Putty, putty, putty!" she called for that was all she could say, as she had not learned to speak English. And, when once she had the cat on her lap, the Queen would not have parted with her for all the gold in Barbary.

So the King made a bargain with the Captain to buy all the goods on the ship; but, for Dick Whittington's cat, he paid ten times as much as for all the goods put together. Then the Captain took leave of the King and Queen of Barbary, and set sail again for England.

One morning, some months later, Mr. Fitzwarren in his counting-house was counting out his money, when he heard someone tap on the door.

"Who's there?" he demanded.

'A friend," the answer came. "A friend, with news of your good ship 'Unicorn.'"

Mr. Fitzwarren hastened to open the door at once and there stood the Captain before him, with a bill-of-lading in one hand and a box of jewels in the other. So full of joy was the merchant at learning of the safe return of his ship, that he most devoutly thanked Heaven for sending him such good fortune.

The first story the Captain told was about Mistress Puss and her fate; and he showed his master all the rich payment the King had made in exchange for poor Dick's cat. As soon as Mr. Fitzwarren heard this remarkable tale, he called out loudly to his servants:

> "Go send him in, and tell him of his fame;
> Pray call him *Mr. Whittington* by name!"

Dick was scouring pots for the cook when word was brought to him that he was summoned to the counting-house to go before his master.

"To the counting-house! I can't go! I'm too dirty!" cried Dick in dismay. But he was bidden to go as he was, in his working clothes, all the same.

No sooner had he appeared than Mr. Fitzwarren addressed him as Mr. Whittington and he ordered a chair to be set for him. Then the lad thought surely his master and the men must be poking fun at him.

"Don't poke fun at a simple lad! Let me go back to work," said he.

"Mr. Whittington," said Mr. Fitzwarren, "no one is poking fun at you. This is what has happened. The Captain has sold your cat to the King of Barbary and, in return for her, he has brought you more riches than all I have put together."

Then he bade his men open the treasure chest and show Dick what was in it. The poor boy could not believe his eyes. He begged his master to take at least a part of the treasure, but Mr. Fitzwarren said, "No, it is all your own. I feel sure you will use it well."

Next Dick asked Mistress Alice to take some of the jewels, but she, too, said no and thanked him.

"Your good fortune makes me happy, and you've deserved it all!" she said.

So Dick made presents to the Captain, the sailors, and the servants in Mr. Fitzwarren's household. And when his face was washed, and his hair was curled, and he was dressed in a fine suit of clothes, he appeared as handsome a youth as one could wish to see.

Some years after this, there was a splendid wedding at one of the beautiful churches in London. Mistress Alice became the wife of Mr. Richard Whittington. And the lord mayor was there and the great judges and the sheriffs and many more besides. But Richard Whittington, in spite of his great fortune, worked on as diligently as ever. He was first a successful merchant, then sheriff of the city, and thrice lord mayor of London. King Henry V bestowed upon him the honor of knighthood, and he became Sir Richard Whittington. Thus, by going back to his work, no matter how hard he found it, he proved the words of the great bells of Bow to be true when they called him "Whittington, thrice Lord Mayor of London."

JAMIE WATT
and the
GIANT in the
TEAKETTLE

Jamie Watt had made a little wooden cart with wheels. Holding it in his hands, he sat before the fire in his grandmother's kitchen in Scotland. He was thinking only of his cart when suddenly he looked up and noticed something strange, something so queer he forgot all about the cart. Over the rosy flames on the hearth hung his grandmother's teakettle. There was nothing strange about that. It had hung there ever since Jamie could remember. But what was happening in that kettle now? As the water in it boiled, sending white puffs of steam from its spout, something wonderful was happening, something that Jamie had never noticed before.

S-s-s, S-s-s! Piff, Piff! the lid of the kettle rattled, then something lifted it up, up into the air.

"Grandma, what is there inside your kettle?" Jamie cried in great excitement.

Grandma was busy laying the table for supper.

45

"Nothing but water, Jamie!" she answered.

S-s-s, S-s-s! Piff, Piff! Up popped the lid again.

"But Grandma, there must be something inside the kettle," Jamie insisted. "Something keeps lifting the lid! What is it, Grandma? What is it?"

"Maybe you think there's a brownie or a pixie in the kettle!" Grandma laughed. "No, lad, no! It's only the steam that does the lifting! See! Clouds of steam are puffing out all around the lid!"

Now Jamie wasn't thinking at all that there was a brownie or a pixie in the kettle. He was thinking that there was some kind of a giant there, a giant stronger and more powerful than any Granny had ever told him about when she got going on her very best giant tales. Rising, he carefully lifted the lid by its knob and looked in the kettle. Nothing did he see but boiling, bubbling water. That made him still more curious.

"Steam—where does it come from?" he demanded. "How did it get inside the kettle?"

"Why, dearie," Grandma answered, "steam rises from water whenever water boils."

For a little longer Jamie stood studying the kettle, then he sat down again, and while he was thinking he began absent-mindedly spinning the wheels of his cart.

"Grandma!" he burst out at last. "If the steam in that kettle is strong enough to lift the lid, why couldn't steam from a lot more water lift heavier things? Why couldn't it even push wheels around?"

Push wheels around? That was so absurd a question

46

Grandma didn't even try to answer it. Jamie had strange and idle dreams, she thought, and she wished he would spend his time thinking of something more useful than pushing wheels around with steam. But Jamie never left off wondering about that mysterious giant, Steam.

"If I could only find out how to make use of all its enormous power," he told himself, "it might lift heavy weights. It might even make machinery go and move a cart along without the need of a horse."

So Jamie kept right on trying to learn all he could about steam. When he grew to be a man, he made experiments with steam engines used for pumping water in mines and many times his engines failed to go, but he always learned something new from each failure. Other people thought him a fool and laughed at him.

"Ho, ho! Jamie Watt is going to harness up the clouds that puff out of his granny's teakettle and make them do the work of a giant!" they would jeer. But in spite of all this, Jamie worked on year after year until at last he did indeed make a steam engine that could really turn the wheels of machinery.

It was this engine of Jamie's which made it possible for men who came after him to make the first engines that pushed steamboats and drew trains. For thousands of years men had lived beside that great giant, Steam, yet not one of them had ever learned how to make its mighty power of service to man, till one small boy began to wonder why it lifted the lid off the teakettle in his grandmother's kitchen.

How Robert Fulton Harnessed the Giant

ROBERT FULTON had more ideas than any other boy
in Lancaster, Pennsylvania. He was always design-
ing remarkable things to supply his own boyish wants,
the needs of his mother and his friends. Sometimes he
was late to school and narrowly escaped a trouncing from
the schoolmaster's stout birch rod; but the schoolmaster,
in his secret heart, believed the world would yet hear from
this queer little urchin he often threatened to beat.

When the Fourth of July drew near in 1778, Robert—
then thirteen years old—planned, with the other boys, a
wonderful celebration in honor of the second anniversary
of the Declaration of Independence. The men of the town
were still fighting in the American Revolution; and the boys,
in their bubbling devotion to the cause of liberty, planned
to light the whole city splendidly with candles. On the
first of July, however, the city council decreed that, in
such trying times, people must save all they could to give
for the use of the army. And, since tallow for candles
was scarce, they ordered that no one should light a
candle to celebrate the Fourth.

A sad blow that for the boys! They stood before
the signboard announcing this order of the council, their
faces long and sober. Robert Fulton alone wasted no
time in regrets. He stood for a few moments lost in
thought, then he hurried home and buried himself for a
time in a book. Afterwards he went to the brushmakers

and exchanged his candles for gunpowder. At a second shop, he bought cardboard.

"What are you going to do with cardboard?" asked the clerk in the second shop.

"We are forbidden to light the streets with candles," the boy answered eagerly, "so I'm going to light the sky with rockets!"

"Light the sky! Why, that's impossible!" The man laughed heartily for fireworks were at that time almost unknown in America, though they had long been used in China.

"Impossible!" cried the boy. "Nothing is impossible!" And he marched off home with his purchases.

When darkness came on the Fourth, the boys gathered in the square and built a gigantic bonfire. Their shouts and the leaping of the flames summoned everyone to the square. A row of cardboard cylinders attached to sticks, lay on the grass. Under Robert's direction the boys had made these cylinders, taking the utmost care to have them the right length and thickness, with the stick just the proper length in proportion to the size of the cylinders. The rockets were filled with gunpowder and a number of little balls, made by Robert himself out of such stuff as he knew would produce colored fire. All this Robert had carefully worked out from the general description in his book.

The boys set off the rockets. A loud report, then a streak of fire shot hissing up in the air to burst gloriously in the sky with a great bouquet of stars!

Everyone thanked Robert Fulton, who had worked out that celebration; and the boys, themselves, felt that rockets proved to be better than candles as a means of venting their spirits and celebrating the Fourth. After this, Robert continued experimenting with things and haunting the factories where arms were made for the Continental Army. He had so many ideas, he drew his plans so well, that he often gave older workmen valuable suggestions.

Always and eternally he was experimenting. Sometimes he worked quite mysteriously on problems he would not discuss with his fellows. Once, he continued day after day to go to the druggist's for quicksilver. Great was the curiosity to know what he could be doing with that strange metal that acts as if bewitched. No one ever found out. He kept it a secret, but his comrades thenceforth nicknamed him "Quicksilver Bob."

In 1779, when Robert was fourteen, he met, among the factory youths, a lad who rejoiced in the name of Christopher Gumpf. Now Christopher liked to fish and he kept an old flatboat padlocked to a tree on the banks of the Conestoga Creek. On holidays, he and Robert would set out with bait and lunch for a glorious day upstream. The flatboat was pushed by a pole, and the boys took turns at poling. But it was a tedious task to push the clumsy, old scow for any distance upstream, so Robert's active mind began to work on the problem of how men could more easily make a boat move through the water. While he was thinking of this, he went to visit an aunt

and at her home in New Britain, he entertained himself by making a model of a boat to be propelled by paddles at the sides. The model was too large for Robert to carry home, so he left it in his aunt's attic. Little did she guess, when she found the strange contraption, that in after years it would be her most cherished possession!

Robert confided to Christopher his plan for moving a boat by means of paddle wheels; so, after much secret hammering in the woods by the river, the lads made a set of side paddles, to move their old friend, the scow. The paddle wheels were joined by a bar and worked by a crank. One boy, standing in the center of the boat, could turn the crank, which turned the bar, which turned the paddle wheels, which made the boat go forward!

When the contrivance was finished, Christopher himself could hardly believe it would work; but Robert, with no doubts at all, stepped into the boat, laid hold of the crank and turned it. Off went the scow gliding along upstream.

For a day of delighted triumph, the boys enjoyed their success. Very little effort now sent the boat a long distance. It was much easier and faster than the old-fashioned method of poling. Only a few people stopped to stare at Robert's queer invention, never dreaming what it would lead to, but it was then and there that young Robert Fulton began to plan easier ways to make boats move in the water.

In time he began experimenting with steam, for even the swiftest sailing ships could make little headway when the wind was contrary, or in a calm, or when they were going upstream against the current of a river. Finally, people heard that Fulton was building in a New York shipyard a monstrous kind of boat with great paddles on either side and to make her go, he was installing a steam engine in her. "She'll either refuse to budge or blow up with a bang!" people laughed. And though Fulton called his boat the *Clermont*, the people scornfully called her "Fulton's Folly."

At last it was announced that on August eleventh, 1807, the *Clermont* would make her first run up the Hudson from New York City to Albany and crowds gathered on the wharf where she lay moored, hooting and jeering at "Fulton's Folly." But to their astonishment, when her engine began to chug and her moorings were cast loose, "Fulton's Folly" started to move. Then as she steamed steadily along, the on-lookers turned their jeering into a noisy outburst of cheers.

Past the old sailing ships she chugged, her side paddles churning up water, her tall smokestack belching forth smoke, along with sparks and tongues of flame from the wood fire that made the steam to drive her engine.

Off she went, heading for Albany. With the wind and the current of the Hudson both against her, she still proceeded upstream at the unbelievable speed of five miles an hour.

All the way to Albany crowds lined the riverbank to gape at the first successful steamboat ever launched. And to those watching crowds, the *Clermont* puffed out her message that the day of sailing ships had ended. The day of steamboats had come. For Robert Fulton had harnessed that powerful giant, Steam, whose possibilities for moving things Jamie Watt had discovered. He had made it move a great boat and changed the whole method of traveling by water. No idle words had he spoken when, as a boy, he told the man who said he could not make a skyrocket, "Nothing is impossible."

*Charlotte's Web

WILBUR'S BOAST

E. B. WHITE

Wilbur, the runt of a litter of spring pigs, was lovingly raised by a little girl, Fern, until he was big enough the following summer to be sold to Uncle Homer Zuckerman. Wilbur was comfortable in his new home, but he was too lonely to be happy—the geese, the lambs, and even Templeton, the rat, were too busy to play with him. Then he found Charlotte, a kind-hearted spider, who became so good a friend to Wilbur that she promised to save his life, somehow, after the sheep warned him about the fall butchering.

A spider's web is stronger than it looks. Although it is made of thin, delicate strands, the web is not easily broken. However, a web gets torn every day by the insects that kick around in it, and a spider must rebuild it when it gets full of holes. Charlotte liked to do her weaving during the late afternoon, and Fern liked to sit nearby and watch. One afternoon she heard a most interesting conversation and witnessed a strange event.

"You have awfully hairy legs, Charlotte," said Wilbur, as the spider busily worked at her task.

"My legs are hairy for a good reason," replied Charlotte. "Furthermore, each leg of mine has seven sections—the coxa, the trochanter, the femur, the patella, the tibia, the metatarsus, and the tarsus."

Wilbur sat bolt upright. "You're kidding," he said. "No, I'm not, either."

"Say those names again, I didn't catch them the first time."

"Coxa, trochanter, femur, patella, tibia, metatarsus, and tarsus."

"Goodness!" said Wilbur, looking down at his own chubby legs. "I don't think *my* legs have seven sections."

"Well," said Charlotte, "you and I lead different lives. You don't have to spin a web. That takes real leg work."

"I could spin a web if I tried," said Wilbur, boasting. "I've just never tried."

"Let's see you do it," said Charlotte. Fern chuckled softly, and her eyes grew wide with love for the pig.

"O.K.," replied Wilbur. "You coach me and I'll spin

one. It must be a lot of fun to spin a web. How do I start?"

"Take a deep breath!" said Charlotte, smiling. Wilbur breathed deeply. "Now climb to the highest place you can get to, like this." Charlotte raced up to the top of the doorway. Wilbur scrambled to the top of the manure pile.

"Very good!" said Charlotte. "Now make an attachment with your spinnerets, hurl yourself into space, and let out a dragline as you go down!"

Wilbur hesitated a moment, then jumped out into the air. He glanced hastily behind to see if a piece of rope was following him to check his fall, but nothing seemed to be happening in his rear, and the next thing he knew he landed with a thump. "Ooomp!" he grunted.

Charlotte laughed so hard her web began to sway.

"What did I do wrong?" asked the pig, when he recovered from his bump.

"Nothing," said Charlotte. "It was a nice try."

"I think I'll try again," said Wilbur, cheerfully. "I believe what I need is a little piece of string to hold me."

The pig walked out to his yard. "You there, Templeton?" he called. The rat poked his head out from under the trough.

"Got a little piece of string I could borrow?" asked Wilbur. "I need it to spin a web."

"Yes, indeed," replied Templeton, who saved string. "No trouble at all. Anything to oblige." He crept down into his hole, pushed the goose egg out of the way, and returned with an old piece of dirty white string. Wilbur examined it.

"That's just the thing," he said. "Tie one end to my tail, will you, Templeton?"

Wilbur crouched low with his thin, curly tail toward the rat. Templeton seized the string, passed it around the end of the pig's tail, and tied two half hitches. Charlotte watched in delight. Like Fern, she was truly fond of Wilbur, whose smelly pen and stale food attracted the flies that she needed, and she was proud to see that he was not a quitter and was willing to try again to spin a web.

While the rat and the spider and the little girl watched, Wilbur climbed again to the top of the manure pile, full of energy and hope.

"Everybody watch!" he cried. And summoning all his strength, he threw himself into the air, headfirst. The string trailed behind him. But as he had neglected to fasten the other end to anything, it didn't really do any good, and Wilbur landed with a thud, crushed and hurt. Tears came to his eyes. Templeton grinned. Charlotte just sat quietly. After a bit she spoke.

"You can't spin a web, Wilbur, and I advise you to put

the idea out of your mind. You lack two things needed for spinning a web."

"What are they?" asked Wilbur, sadly.

"You lack a set of spinnerets, and you lack know-how. But cheer up, you don't need a web. Zuckerman supplies you with three big meals a day. Why should you worry about trapping food?"

Wilbur sighed. "You're ever so much cleverer and brighter than I am, Charlotte. I guess I was just trying to show off. Serves me right."

Templeton untied his string and took it back to his home. Charlotte returned to her weaving.

"You needn't feel too badly, Wilbur," she said. "Not many creatures can spin webs. Even men aren't as good at it as spiders, although they *think* they're pretty good, and they'll *try* anything. Did you ever hear of the Queensborough Bridge?"

Wilbur shook his head. "Is it a web?"

"Sort of," replied Charlotte. "But do you know how long it took men to build it? Eight whole years. My goodness, I would have starved to death waiting that long. I can make a web in a single evening."

"What do people catch in the Queensborough Bridge —bugs?" asked Wilbur.

"No," said Charlotte. "They don't catch anything. They just keep trotting back and forth across the bridge thinking there is something better on the other side. If they'd hang head-down at the top of the thing and wait quietly, maybe something good would come along. But no—with men it's rush, rush, rush, every minute. I'm glad I'm a sedentary spider."

"What does sedentary mean?" asked Wilbur.

"Means I sit still a good part of the time and don't go wandering all over creation. I know a good thing when I see it, and my web is a good thing. I stay put and wait for what comes. Gives me a chance to think."

"Well, I'm sort of sedentary myself, I guess," said the pig. "I have to hang around here whether I want to or not. You know where I'd really like to be this evening?"

"Where?"

"In a forest looking for beechnuts and truffles and delectable roots, pushing leaves aside with my wonderful nose, searching and sniffing along the ground, smelling, smelling, smelling . . . "

"You smell just the way you are," remarked a lamb who had just walked in. "I can smell you from here. You're the smelliest creature in the place."

Wilbur hung his head. His eyes grew wet with tears. Charlotte noticed his embarrassment and she spoke sharply to the lamb.

"Let Wilbur alone!" she said. "He has a perfect right to smell, considering his surroundings. You're no bundle of sweet peas yourself. Furthermore, you are interrupting a very pleasant conversation. What were we talking about, Wilbur, when we were so rudely interrupted?"

"Oh, I don't remember," said Wilbur. "It doesn't make any difference. Let's not talk any more for a while, Charlotte. I'm getting sleepy. You go ahead and finish fixing your web and I'll just lie here and watch you. It's a lovely evening." Wilbur stretched out on his side.

Twilight settled over Zuckerman's barn, and a feeling of peace. Fern knew it was almost suppertime but she couldn't bear to leave. Swallows passed on silent wings, in and out of the doorways, bringing food to their young ones. From across the road a bird sang "Whippoorwill, whippoorwill!" Lurvy sat down under an apple tree and lit his pipe; the animals sniffed the familiar smell of strong tobacco. Wilbur heard the trill of the tree toad and the occasional slamming of the kitchen door. All these sounds made him feel comfortable and happy, for he loved life and loved to be a part of the world on a summer evening. But as he lay there he remembered what the old sheep had told him. The thought of death came to him and he began to tremble with fear.

"Charlotte?" he said, softly.

"Yes, Wilbur?"

"I don't want to die."

"Of course you don't," said Charlotte in a comforting voice.

"I just love it here in the barn," said Wilbur. "I love everything about this place."

"Of course you do," said Charlotte. "We all do."

The goose appeared, followed by her seven goslings. They thrust their little necks out and kept up a musical whistling, like a tiny troupe of pipers. Wilbur listened to the sound with love in his heart.

"Charlotte?" he said.

"Yes?" said the spider.

"Were you serious when you promised you would keep them from killing me?"

"I was never more serious in my life. I am not going to let you die, Wilbur."

"How are you going to save me?" asked Wilbur, whose

curiosity was very strong on this point.

"Well," said Charlotte, vaguely, "I don't really know. But I'm working on a plan."

"That's wonderful," said Wilbur. "How is the plan coming, Charlotte? Have you got very far with it? Is it coming along pretty well?" Wilbur was trembling again, but Charlotte was cool and collected.

"Oh, it's coming all right," she said, lightly. "The plan is still in its early stages and hasn't completely shaped up yet, but I'm working on it."

"When do you work on it?" begged Wilbur.

"When I'm hanging head-down at the top of my web. That's when I do my thinking, because then all the blood is in my head."

"I'd be only too glad to help in any way I can."

"Oh, I'll work it out alone," said Charlotte. "I can think better if I think alone."

"All right," said Wilbur. "But don't fail to let me know if there's anything I can do to help, no matter how slight."

"Well," replied Charlotte, "you must try to build yourself up. I want you to get plenty of sleep, and stop worrying. Never hurry and never worry! Chew your food thoroughly and eat every bit of it, except you must leave enough for Templeton. Gain weight and stay well —that's the way you can help. Keep fit, and don't lose your nerve. Do you think you understand?"

"Yes, I understand," said Wilbur.

"Go along to bed, then," said Charlotte. "Sleep is important."

Wilbur trotted over to the darkest corner of his pen

and threw himself down. He closed his eyes. In another minute he spoke.

"Charlotte?" he said.

"Yes, Wilbur?"

"May I go out to my trough and see if I left any of my supper? I think I left just a tiny bit of mashed potato."

"Very well," said Charlotte. "But I want you in bed again without delay."

Wilbur started to race out to his yard.

"Slowly, slowly!" said Charlotte. "Never hurry and never worry!"

Wilbur checked himself and crept slowly to his trough. He found a bit of potato, chewed it carefully, swallowed it, and walked back to bed. He closed his eyes and was silent for a while.

"Charlotte?" he said, in a whisper.

"Yes?"

"May I get a drink of milk? I think there are a few drops of milk in my trough."

"No, the trough is dry, and I want you to go to sleep. No more talking! Close your eyes and go to sleep!"

Wilbur shut his eyes. Fern got up from her stool and started for home, her mind full of everything she had seen and heard.

"Good night, Charlotte!" said Wilbur.

"Good night, Wilbur!"

There was a pause.

"Good night, Charlotte!"

"Good night, Wilbur!"

"Good night!"

"Good night!"

CASEY JONES*

A Song of the Railroad Men

Come all you fellows, for I want you to hear
The story told of a brave engineer.
Casey Jones was the fellow's name,
On a big eight-wheeler of a mighty fame.

Caller called Casey 'bout half past four,
And he kissed his wife at the station door;
Climbed to the cab with his orders in his hand;
Said, "Boys, this is my trip to the Holy Land."

The rain had been coming down for five or six weeks.
The railroad track was like the bed of a creek.
They slowed the train down to a thirty-mile gait,
Made the south-bound mail some eight hours late.

Fireman says, "Casey, you're running too fast.
You ran the block signal, last station you passed."
Casey says, "Yes, but we'll make it though,
For she steams a lot better than I ever know."

Casey says, "Fireman, don't you fret,
Keep knockin' at the fire door, don't give up yet!
I'm goin' to run this train till she leaves the rail,
Or make it on time with the south-bound mail!"

*This song of the railroad men, first sung by a crew in a roundhouse, depicted in true ballad style the dangers and tragedies of early railroading. When Casey Jones was killed in a wreck near Memphis, more verses were added with Casey as the hero.

He pulled back the throttle for Reno Hill,
The whistle for the crossing was awful shrill,
The switchman knew by the engine's moans
That the man at the throttle was Casey Jones.

He rounded the curve within a mile of the place,
Old No. 4 stared him right in the face,
He turned to his fireman said, "Boy, you'd better jump
'Cause there's two locomotives that are going to bump!"

Poor Casey Jones was sure all right,
He stuck to his duty day and night.
Fireman jumped off, but Casey stayed on—
A good engineer, but he's dead and gone.

Headaches and heartaches and all kinds of pain
Are never apart from a railroad train.
Stories of brave men, noble and grand
Belong to the life of a railroad man.

Wilbur Wright and Orville Wright*

ROSEMARY AND STEPHEN VINCENT BENÉT

SAID Orville Wright to Wilbur Wright,
  "These birds are very trying.
I'm sick of hearing them cheep-cheep
About the fun of flying.
A bird has feathers, it is true.
That much I freely grant.
But, must that stop us, W?"
Said Wilbur Wright, "It shan't."
And so they built a glider, first,
And then they built another.
—There never were two brothers more
Devoted to each other.
They ran a dusty little shop
For bicycle-repairing,
And bought each other soda-pop
and praised each other's daring.
They glided here, they glided there,
They sometimes skinned their noses.
—For learning how to rule the air
Was not a bed of roses—

But each would murmur, afterward,
While patching up his bro.
"Are we discouraged, W?"
"Of course we are not, O!"
And finally, at Kitty Hawk
In Nineteen-Three (let's cheer it!)
The first real airplane really flew
With Orville there to steer it!
—And kingdoms may forget their kings
And dogs forget their bites,
But, not till Man forgets his wings,
Will men forget the Wrights.

Getting their early knowledge of mechanics in a bicycle repair shop, Orville and Wilbur Wright produced the first airplane of practical usefulness. After spending years experimenting, they made their first successful flight in 1903, at Kitty Hawk.

Winnie-the-Pooh

IN WHICH POOH GOES VISITING AND GETS INTO A TIGHT PLACE

A. A. MILNE

Edward Bear, known to his friends as Winnie-the-Pooh, or Pooh for short, was walking through the forest one day, humming proudly to himself. He had made up a little hum that very morning, as he was doing his Stoutness Exercises in front of the glass: *Tra-la-la, tra-la-la,* as he stretched up as high as he could go, and then *Tra-la-la, tra-la—oh, help!—la,* as he tried to reach his toes. After breakfast he had said it over and over to himself until he had learnt it off by heart, and now he was humming it right through, properly. It went like this:

> *Tra-la-la, tra-la-la,*
> *Tra-la-la, tra-la-la,*
> *Rum-tum-tiddle-um-tum.*
>   *Tiddle-iddle, tiddle-iddle,*
>   *Tiddle-iddle, tiddle-iddle,*
> *Rum-tum-tum-tiddle-um.*

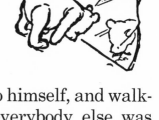

Well, he was humming this hum to himself, and walking along gaily, wondering what everybody else was doing, and what it felt like, being somebody else, when suddenly he came to a sandy bank, and in the bank was a large hole.

"Aha!" said Pooh. (*Rum-tum-tiddle-um-tum.*) "If I know anything about anything, that hole means Rabbit," he said, "and Rabbit means Company," he said, "and Company means Food and Listening-to Me-Humming and such like. *Rum-tum-tum-tiddle-um.*"

So he bent down, put his head into the hole, and called out:

"Is anybody at home?"

There was a sudden scuffling noise from inside the hole, and then silence.

"What I said was, 'Is anybody at home?'" called out Pooh very loudly.

"No!" said a voice; and then added, "You needn't shout so loud. I heard you quite well the first time."

"Bother!" said Pooh. "Isn't there anybody here at all?"

"Nobody."

Winnie-the-Pooh took his head out of the hole, and thought for a little, and he thought to himself, "There must be somebody there, because somebody must have *said* 'Nobody.'" So he put his head back in the hole, and said:

"Hallo, Rabbit, isn't that you?"

"No," said Rabbit, in a different sort of voice this time.

"But isn't that Rabbit's voice?"

"I don't *think* so," said Rabbit. "It isn't *meant* to be."

"Oh!" said Pooh.

He took his head out of the hole, and had another think, and then he put it back, and said:

"Well, could you very kindly tell me where Rabbit is?"

"He has gone to see his friend Pooh Bear, who is a great friend of his."

"But this *is* Me!" said Bear, very much surprised.

"What sort of Me?"

"Pooh Bear."

"Are you sure?" said Rabbit, still more surprised.

"Quite, quite sure," said Pooh.

"Oh, well, then, come in."

So Pooh pushed and pushed and pushed his way through the hole, and at last he got in.

"You were quite right," said Rabbit, looking at him all over. "It *is* you. Glad to see you."

"Who did you think it was?"

"Well, I wasn't sure. You know how it is in the Forest.

One can't have *anybody* coming into one's house. One has to be *careful.* What about a mouthful of something?"

Pooh always liked a little something at eleven o'clock in the morning, and he was very glad to see Rabbit getting out the plates and mugs; and when Rabbit said, "Honey or condensed milk with your bread?" he was so excited that he said, "Both," and then, so as not to seem greedy, he added, "But don't bother about the bread, please." And for a long time after that he said nothing . . . until at last, humming to himself in a rather sticky voice, he got up, shook Rabbit lovingly by the paw, and said that he must be going on.

"Must you?" said Rabbit politely.

"Well," said Pooh, "I could stay a little longer if it— if you—" and he tried very hard to look in the direction of the larder.

"As a matter of fact," said Rabbit, "I was going out myself directly."

"Oh, well, then, I'll be going on. Good-bye."

"Well, good-bye, if you're sure you won't have any more."

"*Is* there any more?" asked Pooh quickly.

Rabbit took the covers off the dishes, and said, "No, there wasn't."

"I thought not," said Pooh, nodding to himself. "Well, good-bye. I must be going on."

So he started to climb out of the hole. He pulled with his front paws, and pushed with his back paws, and in a little while his nose was out in the open again . . . and then his ears . . . and then front paws . . . and then his shoulders . . . and then—

71

"Oh, help!" said Pooh. "I'd better go back."

"Oh, bother!" said Pooh. "I shall have to go on."

"I can't do either!" said Pooh. "Oh, help *and* bother!"

Now by this time Rabbit wanted to go for a walk too, and finding the front door full, he went out by the back door, and came round to Pooh, and looked at him.

"Hallo, are you stuck?" he asked.

"N-no," said Pooh carelessly. "Just resting and think-ing and humming to myself."

"Here, give us a paw."

Pooh Bear stretched out a paw, and Rabbit pulled and pulled and pulled. . . .

"*Ow!*" cried Pooh. "You're hurting!"

"The fact is," said Rabbit, "you're stuck."

"It all comes," said Pooh crossly, "of not having front doors big enough."

"It all comes," said Rabbit sternly, "of eating too much. I thought at the time," said Rabbit, "only I didn't like to say anything," said Rabbit, "that one of us was eating too much," said Rabbit, "and I knew it wasn't *me,*" he said. "Well, well, I shall go and fetch Christopher Robin."

Christopher Robin lived at the other end of the Forest, and when he came back with Rabbit, and saw the front half of Pooh, he said, "Silly old Bear," in such a loving voice that everybody felt quite hopeful again.

"I was just beginning to think," said Bear, sniffing slightly, "that Rabbit might never be able to use his front door again. And I should *hate* that," he said.

"So should I," said Rabbit.

"Use his front door again?" said Christopher Robin. "Of course he'll use his front door again."

"Good," said Rabbit.

"If we can't pull you out, Pooh, we might push you back."

Rabbit scratched his whiskers thoughtfully, and pointed out that, when once Pooh was pushed back, he was back, and of course nobody was more glad to see Pooh than *he* was, still there it was, some lived in trees and some lived underground, and—

"You mean I'd *never* get out?" said Pooh.

"I mean," said Rabbit, "that having got *so* far, it seems a pity to waste it."

Christopher Robin nodded.

"Then there's only one thing to be done," he said. "We shall have to wait for you to get thin again."

"How long does getting thin take?" asked Pooh anxiously.

"About a week, I should think."

"But I can't stay here for a *week!*"

"You can *stay* here all right, silly old Bear. It's getting you out which is so difficult."

"We'll read to you," said Rabbit cheerfully. "And I hope it won't snow," he added. "And I say, old fellow, you're taking up a good deal of room in my house—*do* you mind if I use your back legs as a towel-horse? Because, I mean, there they are—doing nothing—and it would be very convenient just to hang the towels on them."

"A week!" said Pooh gloomily. *"What about meals?"*

"I'm afraid no meals," said Christopher Robin, "because of getting thin quicker. But we *will* read to you."

Bear began to sigh, and then found he couldn't because he was so tightly stuck; and a tear rolled down his eye, as he said:

"Then would you read a Sustaining Book, such as would help and comfort a Wedged Bear in Great Tightness?"

So for a week Christopher Robin read that sort of book at the North end

of Pooh, and Rabbit hung his washing on the South end ... and in between Bear felt himself getting slenderer and slenderer. And at the end of the week Christopher Robin said, *"Now!"*

So he took hold of Pooh's front paws and Rabbit took hold of Christopher Robin, and all Rabbit's friends and relations took hold of Rabbit, and they all pulled together. ...

And for a long time Pooh only said *"Ow!"* ... And *"Oh!"* ...

And then, all of a sudden, he said *"Pop!"* just as if a cork were coming out of a bottle.

And Christopher Robin and Rabbit and all Rabbit's friends and relations went head-over-heels backwards ... and on the top of them came Winnie-the-Pooh—free!

So, with a nod of thanks to his friends he went on with his walk through the forest, humming proudly to himself. But, Christopher Robin looked after him lovingly, and said to himself, "Silly old Bear!"

How Jack Sought the Golden Apples
An English Folk Tale

ONCE the King of England fell sick and the wisemen said that nothing would make him well but to eat of some golden apples that could only be found in a far distant country. Then the King's eldest son said to the next eldest son:

"Let's get those apples! For if we do, we'll raise ourselves high in our father's favor! He'll give us castles and treasures, gold and silver and jewels!"

"Aye!" said the second son. "Those apples would truly profit us much!" Then Jack, the youngest son, said:

"I'd seek the apples, too! But only because I wish with all my heart to see our father well again!"

"As always, you're a fool!" the eldest cried. "You'll never get anywhere if you take no thought for yourself!"

"Be that as it may!" Jack answered. And the next day he set out on horseback with his brothers. But at the first cross-road the two eldest said to Jack:

"We're taking the road to the right! We'll have you with us no longer! You must take the turn to the left!"

"That's all right with me!" Jack answered.
And off he went by himself.

OVER THE HILLS

Over hill and dale he rode, far and afar away. Then one night he came to a tumble-down house near a forest and by the door sat an ugly old man. He had long gray hair, his teeth were curling out of his mouth and his finger and toenails had not been cut for a hundred years.

"Good evening, my King's son!" said the old man.

"Good evening, sir!" Jack answered, trembling a little at seeing such an ugly old fellow.

But when he had stabled his horse at the old man's bidding and the two were eating supper, all Jack's fear died down, for under the old man's terrifying appearance he was in truth a lovable fellow. At last he said:

"Jack, I know you're seeking the golden apples to make your father well. In this search I can help you. But you'll have to stay here tonight! And it won't be too pleasant for you! Frogs and snakes will crawl over you! But mind you, you mustn't so much as stir, for if you do, you'll be turned into a frog or a snake yourself!"

At that Jack shivered again. But he got up his courage and went to bed. Then it happened just as the old man had said. Snakes crawled over him, frogs hopped on his body. They bit and stung him! But he never stirred. And next morning when the old man asked, "Well, son, how are you?" Jack replied, "Very well, thank you!"

"Good!" the old man cried. "You've got on well so far! Now you must go on to my next eldest brother!"

Then the old man brought out a fresh horse and gave Jack a ball of yarn, bidding him to throw it between the horse's ears and follow wherever it led. So Jack flung the ball between the horse's ears and off he went like the wind. Thus he came at last to the next brother's house which was as tumble-down as the first one's had been. And the old man here was even uglier than his brother. However, he put Jack's horse in his stable, gave the youth plenty to eat and talked most kindly to him. At last he said:

"Son, I'll send word to my eldest brother. He'll be able to send you on to the place where the golden apples are. But tonight you mustn't stir, no matter what happens!"

So Jack went to bed and bore all the crawlings, the hoppings, the bites and stings again. But next morning he was as hearty and well as ever. Then the old man brought a fresh horse and a new ball of yarn. Telling Jack that he had sent word to his eldest brother, he bade the youth to be on his way. "For," said he, "you have much more to go through before you get those apples!"

So Jack flung the ball and off he went like lightning till he came to the eldest brother's house. This old man was as ugly as the others but after supper he said:

"My son, in this house nothing will disturb you. To-night you'll sleep well that you may be wide awake tomorrow. For tomorrow is the great day! The day when you will either fail or succeed in this venture you've undertaken! And 'tis only by heeding every word of my instructions that you'll come back alive!"

"Speak!" Jack answered. "I shall heed you!"

"Well this is what you must do!" the old man said. "You must start out early, for you'll have to go and come in one day, since there's no safe spot for you to rest within thousands of miles of that place. When you draw near it you will see a big castle, surrounded by coal black water. Then tie your horse to a tree. Three white swans will be floating on the black water and you must say, 'Swan, swan, carry me over in the name of the Griffin of the Greenwood!' At that the swans will take you to the castle. There you will have to pass three gates. The first will be guarded by dragons, the second by lions, the third by giants. So mind this well, you must be there exactly at one o'clock and leave precisely at two, for all these dread creatures sleep between one and two!"

"I shall do exactly as you say!" Jack answered.

"And when you enter the castle," the old man went on, "you'll see some grand rooms but you must go down to the kitchen and out through a door on your left. There you'll find a garden in which the golden apples grow! Pick them! Put them in your wallet! Then hurry back as you came! Once you get on your horse, you'll hear a terrible yelling behind you. 'Twill be all those monsters chasing you! But don't look back! Not once! For if you do they'll overtake you. But if you don't, they'll chase you for no more than a thousand miles! Then you'll hear all the noise die down and you'll know you've routed them forever! For they'll vanish into thin air!"

"In all things I shall obey you!" Jack answered.

Then he went to bed, and had a good rest. The next morning the old man brought out a fresh horse and gave Jack one last bit of advice.

"Should you see in that castle a pretty young lady," he said, "don't stay with her too long or your hour will run out! And don't awaken her either! For if you do all those monsters will wake up too!"

But Jack had never yet set eyes on any young lady who made his heart beat the faster. So he laughed:

"Hah, hah! No lady could keep me long in such a castle!"

And off he went like a shot from a gun. Then at last he saw the castle surrounded by black water on which three beautiful white swans were floating. Dismounting, he looked at his watch. It was one o'clock exactly. So he tied his horse to a tree and cried, "Swan, swan, carry me over in the name of the Griffin of the Greenwood."

At once the swans flew to him. He caught hold of the tail of one while the others bore him up, one on either side. In a twinkling they had him over the water. Then he saw the first gate which was guarded by dragons. But the dragons were fast asleep, so he passed them safely and he went as safely by the lions and giants which guarded the other two gates, for they were all fast asleep.

So far, so good! But as he walked through the grand rooms in the castle on his way to the kitchen, he suddenly saw a sight that halted him in his tracks. Through an open door he saw the loveliest maiden in the world, lying fast asleep on a golden bedstead. On tiptoe he entered the room and stole quietly up to her. And so beautiful was she that he stood for some time just looking down on her golden hair which streamed out on the pillow. Then he took out his big watch and exchanged it for her little watch. He took out his big pocket handkerchief and exchanged it for her little handkerchief. And bending down, he kissed her. At that her eyelids flickered. But with a little sigh, she sank back to sleep again.

And now Jack had lost so much time that he had to hurry. Down to the kitchen he ran and out to the garden where he saw those golden apples shining on a tree. Picking them, he put them in his wallet, then hastened to retrace his steps. But as he returned through the kitchen the cook, who had been lying asleep on the floor, was beginning to move, her hand which held a huge knife was twitching and she was almost awake.

Racing with time, Jack ran on at breakneck speed, for
his hour was nearly up. As he passed through the gates,
the dragons, the lions and the giants were all beginning
to stir and yawn. But he called for the swans and they
got him across the black water at precisely two o'clock.

Mounting his horse, Jack was off like a streak. And in
no time he heard behind him that yelling of which the old
man had spoken. But he never looked back, not once!
And after he had gone a thousand miles, the noise died
down, so he knew those terrible monsters had vanished
forever. Thus he came safely back to the tumble-down
house of the eldest of the three brothers.

82

Gladly the old man heard his tale of what had happened. Then he led the youth off to a well. And Jack felt
very sorry for him, for he could scarcely walk because his
long toenails curled up like ram's horns. When they came
to the well the old man gave Jack a sword and said:

"Cut off my head and throw it in the well!"

"Nay, nay! I can't do that!" Jack cried in alarm.

But the old man insisted. So Jack cut off his head and
threw it in the well. Then to his astonishment, a fine
young man climbed from the well while the hut became a
mansion. And the young man said with joy:

"Jack, 'twas a wicked magician who turned me into
that ugly old man and changed my mansion into that
tumble-down hut. From his evil spells I could escape only
by finding a friend who would cut off my head and throw
it in the well. The same is true of my brothers. You must
serve them as you
have served me!"

So Jack rode on and
served the other brothers
as he had the first. Then
he rode on to the cross-
roads where he had left
his own brothers. And
there, being weary, he
tied his horse to his leg,
put his golden apples under
his head and lay down to rest.

83

Thus Jack was fast asleep when his two brothers came riding along. Now they had found no golden apples, so they had picked some common apples and got a goldsmith to gild them until they looked like gold. And when they saw Jack asleep they took his apples out from under his head. Finding them to be pure gold, they slipped their own apples under his head. Then off they went, feeling very clever, to return to their father's palace in London.

Well, by-and-by Jack woke up. His apples didn't seem any different from those he had put under his head before he went to sleep. So he started out for London full of joy, thinking he was taking to his father what would make him well again. He was nearing the city when he heard all the bells of London ringing as though to proclaim some glad tidings. And when he reached his father's side, he found that the bells had been telling the people their King was recovered. For he had eaten of those golden apples which his elder sons had brought him.

"Father!" cried Jack. "I'm happy to see you well again! But, I, too, brought you some apples! I pray you to taste them just that you may know I also tried to bring you what you needed!"

At that the older sons frowned darkly. They had no mind to let their younger brother find his right place in his father's affections. So knowing well what kind of apples they had left with Jack, they cried out:

"Father! This young rascal would have you eat his apples that he may poison you and kill you!"

And taking from Jack the common apples which they had had gilded, they showed the King, how under the outer coating of gold, these apples were black and rotting. Poisonous enough they looked! And the King was first hurt then angry to think that Jack would actually try to poison him. Summoning his headsman he cried:

"Take this youth away! Cut off his head!"

So the headsman took Jack off, while the poor youth remained wholly mystified as to what had happened to his apples. But the headsman liked Jack and he could not bear to cut off his head. So he led the youth to the woods and left him there. Jack was wandering along alone, with no weapon to defend himself when he saw a big bear coming toward him. Quickly he climbed a tree and tried to hide. But the bear came on, lunged heavily against the tree and gave it a shake that almost sent Jack headlong out of the branches. Then the bear could see his face plainly and all at once that bear laughed.

"Come on down, friend!" he cried. "I know you now! You're the King's youngest son! As for me I'm not really a bear, I'm Prince Jubal dressed up in a bearskin! Over yonder I live with a merry crowd of youths and maidens. And I only wear my bearskin to scare off strangers. For we'll have with us none, save good, bold, jolly young fellows. But you, you're welcome to our midst!"

So Jack climbed down while Jubal got out of his bearskin. And when Jack told Jubal how he had been condemned to death, Jubal answered:

"You shall live with me and my friends! And while
you're with us, no evil can befall you!"

Then he led Jack to a group of white tents set up in a
lovely green glade in the forest. Before the tents many
youths and maidens were dancing and making merry
and when Jubal presented Jack, they all bade him
welcome. So for many days Jack lived with Jubal and
his friends. Hunting, singing, dancing, laughing, he
shared their joyous life in the greenwood. But often when
he was alone by night he took out the little gold watch
and the small white handkerchief which he had taken as
keepsakes from the sleeping maiden in the castle. Then
he wished with all his heart that he could see her again.

Meantime the maiden—Princess of Melvales she was—
had awakened after Jack left to find, to her own astonish-

ment, that all those lions, giants and dragons which had kept her a prisoner in her own palace, had suddenly vanished and left her free. Next she discovered that her watch and handkerchief were gone and that in their place she had a man's big watch and a man's big pocket handkerchief. And the more she thought about these strange things the more clearly she seemed to remember that she had seen, as in a dream, a handsome youth bend over and kiss her. Then she found engraved on the watch the words, "To my son! From the King of England." So she guessed that one of the sons of the King had paid her a visit while she slept and accomplished all these wonders. But which son it was she did not know.

And now she heard rumors that the King, egged on by his eldest sons, had somehow got rid of his youngest son. And her heart was roused with pity for that youngest son. Being as spirited as she was lovely, she gathered an army and set out for London to learn the truth of this matter. Leaving her army outside the city, she went to the King and asked him to present his sons to her.

87

Now the King thought she had come to choose one of his sons for her husband, so he gladly summoned his eldest son. Straightway the Princess asked this Prince, "Have you ever been to the Castle of Melvales?"

Then he, thinking that here was a wife who would make him rich, answered her with a lie.

"Yes, my lady!" he said. "I've visited your castle!"

At once she threw Jack's handkerchief down on the floor and bade the Prince to walk over it without stumbling. Well, that didn't seem difficult to do, so he stepped out onto the handkerchief. But the handkerchief knew to whom it belonged. No sooner had he touched it with his foot than he fell down and broke his leg and was carried off screaming. So the King, in great distress, summoned his second son. But when the Princess asked the same question this Prince answered with the same lie. So he, too, stepped on the handkerchief, fell down and broke his leg. Then the Princess looked the King straight in the eye and asked, "Have you not still another son?"

At that the King trembled. For months he had suffered great grief for the loss of his son and now he wondered if the Princess had brought her army because she knew what he had done. At last he summoned his headsman and asked in a whisper:

"My youngest son? Did you behead him?"

"Nay, sire!" the headsman answered. "He is alive!"

"God be praised!" the King cried in great joy. "Then find him and bring him to me at once!"

So the headsman searched the forest until he found Jack in Jubal's camp. Then he brought the youth back to the palace. And when Jack saw before him that lovely Princess of whom he had so long dreamed, his heart leaped within him. Smiling, she said, "Kind sir, have you ever been to the Castle of Melvales?"

"Yes, my lady! Yes!" Jack answered eagerly.

"Then please walk over this handkerchief!" she said.

So Jack walked many times across the handkerchief. He even danced upon it. Gladly the Princess cried:

"Here's the young man I seek!" And she took from a silken purse which hung at her waist the watch he had left her while he took from his pocket her little gold watch and her small white handkerchief. And the two smiled lovingly at each other.

Needless to say the King took Jack back wholly into his love. And he was overjoyed when Jack told him later that he and the Princess were to be married. But he was so angry with his eldest sons that he sent them to prison to cool their heels until they could repent of their evil ways. And he forced them to tell the truth about those golden apples. Thus he learned at last that it was Jack who had gone through so many difficult adventures to get those apples which had made him well again.

So Jack and the Princess were married with Jubal attending their wedding. Then the two bade Jack's father a loving farewell and returned with their army to the Castle of Melvales where they lived happily ever after.

The Red Ettin
A TALE TOLD IN ENGLAND AND SCOTLAND

ONCE there lived a poor widow who had two sons and the time came when the eldest wished to leave home to seek his fortune. So the widow took her last bit of oatmeal and baked a good round bannock. Then she said:

"Son, will you take with you on your journey the whole or the half of this bannock?"

And the youth, thinking only that he might be traveling far and never for a moment thinking that he would be carrying off all the food there was in the house, answered right merrily, "I'll take the whole bannock!"

After that he gave his brother a knife and said:

"Look at this knife every day. If it continues to shine you'll know I'm well. But if it grows rusty, you may be sure that some ill has befallen me."

Then the youth put the bannock under his arm and started out on his journey. He had traveled far when he saw an old woman standing by the roadside.

"Kind sir," she said, "I am very hungry. Will you give me a bit of your bannock?"

But the youth answered, "Nay! I have no more than enough for myself." And he left her and went on his way.

The next afternoon he met an old man who was tending sheep and he asked to whom the sheep belonged.

"To the dread Red Ettin of Ireland!" the shepherd answered. Then he started to sing in a sad, mournful voice:

"The Red Ettin of Ireland
  Once lived in Ballygan,
He stole King Malcolm's daughter,
  The King of fair Scotland.
He beats her, he binds her,
  He lays her on a band;
And every day he strikes her
  With a bright silver wand."

Then the shepherd went on to say that all the country of the Ettin was a very dangerous place. But the youth continued on his way. And in a short time he saw a multitude of beasts plunging toward him. Like great bulls they looked but each of them had two heads and on each head were four great horns. Then the youth was sorely frightened and he ran away in a hurry.

91

Soon he saw a castle rising up on a hill before him and when he reached the place one door was standing open, so he flung himself over the doorstep and found himself in the kitchen. Before the fire an old woman was sitting and when he had recovered his breath the youth asked if he might take shelter for the night in her kitchen.

"Aye, you may stay the night here!" she answered. "But it's no good place to be! For this is the castle of the Red Ettin. And he's a monster, in shape of a man but with three great heads. He spares no earthly man!"

On hearing that, the youth knew not what to do. He feared to leave the place because of those monstrous beasts and he feared to stay because of the monstrous Ettin. But he thought that if he could only hide for the night, he might get safely away in the morning. So he begged the woman to hide him and she showed him a dark little hole behind a pile of wood. But he had scarcely crawled into the hole when the awful Red Ettin came into the kitchen. At once he shouted:

"Snouk but and snouk ban,
I find the smell of an earthly man!"

And with that he started to search the kitchen. In no time he found the poor youth, dragged him out of the hole, held him fast with one hand and roared:

"Answer three questions or you shall die!"

Then the first head asked, "A thing without an end, what's that?" But the young man did not know.

So the second head cried: "The smaller, the more dangerous, what's that?" But the young man did not know.

Lastly the third head cried, "The dead carrying the living: riddle me that?"

But the young man had to give it up. So the Red Ettin took a mallet, knocked him on the head, and turned him into a pillar of stone.

On the morning after this happened, the younger son took out his brother's knife to look at it, as usual, and he was grieved to find it no longer shining but brown with rust. Then he told his mother that the time was come for him to go away on his travels also. So as he had been providing her with meal, she took the last of it and baked a bannock for him. But when she asked the younger son, as she had the older one, whether he would take with him all the bannock or only half, he answered:

"I'll take but half, my mother, for you'll be needing the rest!"

Thus he went away on his journey and after a time he, too, met the old woman by the roadside.

"Kind sir, I am very hungry," she said. "Will you give me a bit of your bannock?"

"Gladly, good dame!" the youth answered. And he gave her a piece of his bannock.

At that the old woman smiled and gave him a magic wand, for she was a fairy. And she told him many things about what would happen to him, and what he must do in all circumstances. Then she vanished out of his sight.

By-and-by he came on the old man herding sheep. And

he, too, heard the mournful song the old shepherd sang about the poor daughter of the King of Scotland, whom the Ettin kept bound in prison and whom he so cruelly beat. Then the youth vowed to himself that he would save that fair Scottish lady. And he went on to the place where the monstrous beasts came plunging toward him. But he didn't run! Not he! He stood his ground and faced them squarely. And when the beasts saw that he refused to run from them, they all turned tail and ran from him.

Thus the younger son came in time to the Ettin's castle and entered the kitchen as the older son had. The old woman by the fire warned him of the terrible Red Ettin but he was not to be daunted. Then they heard the Ettin coming down the hallway. And now he was roaring:

> *"Snouk but and snouk ban,*
> *I find the smell of an earthly man;*
> *Be he living or be he dead,*
> *His heart in the fire shall bake my bread."*

As soon as he came through the doorway he spied the young man. Then he halted to roar that the youth's life would only be spared if he could answer three questions. But the young man had been told the answers by the good fairy. So when the first head asked, "What's a thing without an end?" he said: "A ball!" And when the second head said, "The smaller the more dangerous; what's that?" he replied, "A bridge." And lastly when the third head asked, "When does the dead carry the living?" he answered, "When a wooden ship sails on the sea bearing men."

Then the Red Ettin, finding that the youth could answer all his questions, knew that his power was gone. And he let out a snarl of rage. But the young man seized an axe and cut off all the monster's three heads. After that he asked the old woman to show him where the poor, distressed daughter of the King of Scotland lay; so the old woman took him upstairs. There she opened many doors and out of each came a beautiful lady who had been imprisoned by the Ettin. Loveliest of all, was the daughter of the King of Scotland who gave him a grateful kiss.

Then the old woman took the youth back to the kitchen and showed him the stone pillar, which she said was all that remained of his brother. But the youth had only to touch the pillar with his wand, when his brother came to life, smiled gladly and embraced him.

Next day that whole happy company set out for the castle of the King of Scotland. And when they reached there, the King was so overjoyed to have his daughter back safe that he gave her to the youth in marriage. And then all lived happily ever after.

The Steamboat and the Locomotive[*]

GELETT BURGESS

ON the railway that ran through the City o' Ligg
there was once a locomotive, who was always dis-
contented and grumbling. Nothing in the world was good
enough for him; or, at least, nothing in the City o' Ligg.

His coal was too hard or too soft; it was never just right.
He hated to pull passenger trains because he had to go so
fast, and he didn't like to pull freight trains because they
were too heavy. He was always complaining that he was
out of order, so that he might stay in the Round House
and not work. He would shunt himself on sidings in
hopes he might be forgotten; he was afraid to go over
bridges, for fear they would break down; and he hated
tunnels because they were so dark and cold. He thought
iron rails were too soft to get good hold on, and he said
that steel rails were altogether too slippery. He quarrelled with his tender, and he refused to be coupled up to
one that he didn't fancy. He snorted and hissed at the
semaphores and point signals, and he was a nuisance to
the railway in more ways than can be told.

But, if he were bad, there was a young steamboat on the
river who was worse. She was a very pretty craft, but
that was no reason why she should insist on having a new
set of paddle wheels *every* year. She was absurdly par-
ticular about her funnel, and, if it were not painted the
exact color that she fancied she would declare that she

*Taken from *The Lively City o' Ligg*. Used by permission of the publishers, Frederick A. Stokes Company

would scuttle herself. She would roll and pitch with anger if they tried to back her. She would dig up the muddy bottom of the river with her paddles, and she gave a deal of trouble about steering.

When these ill-natured creatures came together at the dock in the river below the fortifications, they used to complain to each other till the cannon above them would cry, "Oh, I *say*?" and the bridge told them that they ought to be ashamed of themselves.

One day, after the steamboat had been carrying a load of noisy excursionists up from the harbor, she found the locomotive on the pier in a very gloomy state of mind.

"I'm not going to stand this any longer!" he said. "They've put me to hauling coal, and it's no work for a machine like me, especially when I can't burn any of it myself. I'm going to run away!"

"Well, that's a good idea; suppose I go with you, and we'll set out to seek our fortunes!" said the steamer.

They talked it all over, and finally decided to start that very night. The steamboat was to help the locomotive on the water, and the locomotive was to help the steamboat on the land. They were to share their wood and coal and water and have a jolly good time as long as they could.

At midnight the locomotive got on board the boat, and she steamed softly up the river. "This is fun!" said he.

"It's all right for you," said the boat, "but I must say you're heavier than I thought. Wait till it's *your* turn to give *me* a ride. I can't go much farther, anyway, the water is getting shallow. There's a dam up above here, so I think we'd better go ashore now."

She climbed up the bank with the locomotive's assistance, and he then hoisted her up on top of his cab, and set out across the fields. She was a little boat but she was heavy, and the locomotive puffed away with all his might through the grass, stopping to rest once in a while. So they went on for several days, turn and turn about, for they had to cross several lakes on the way.

After awhile, they began to approach a line of hills and the ground grew steeper and steeper, till at last the loco-motive could go no further with the steamboat on his back. So she got off and scrambled along for a few miles with her paddle wheels while the locomotive pushed her

BERT R. ELLIOTT

98

from behind. But the time came when neither of them could go a step further, and they lay on the ground exhausted. To make matters worse, they grew short of water and fuel. They cut down their rations to a ton of coal and a barrel of water a day, and even then they didn't have enough to take them back to either a forest or a lake.

It seemed likely that they would have to perish there on the hillside, and they quarrelled with each other peevishly, each accusing the other of being at fault for suggesting this terrible journey. The old river Wob and the railway of the City o' Ligg had never seemed so pleasant before, but, alas! it was many days' journey away.

Just as they began to think all hope was gone, one of them espied a dot in the sky. It grew larger and larger.

"It is a *balloon*?" they cried together, and they both began to blow their whistles with all the strength of the little steam that was left in their boilers.

The balloon came nearer and nearer, till it had got within hailing distance, and then they saw it was laughing almost hard enough to split its sides. It was a very fat, pink, round balloon, and, as it shook with merriment, its basket swung wildly above them.

"Well, I *declare*?" it cried out. "This is the queerest thing I ever saw! What in the world are you doing away up in these mountains? I never saw a locomotive or a steamboat on top of a hill before!"

"For heaven's sake, please don't laugh like that," cried the steamer, "but come and help us before we perish!"

The balloon finally consented to give them assistance over the mountains, and let down a rope, which the two tied around their waists. The balloon then rose, and the locomotive and steamboat were hoisted high in the air, and they all sailed away toward the East, across the range of mountains. They had floated for half a day in this way, when the balloon gave a pull up, a little harder than usual, and the rope suddenly broke! Down went the two, falling faster and faster and they thought their last moment had come. But, by good luck, they happened to fall in the middle of a large forest, and landed safely in an oak tree, without breaking a piece of machinery. Yet they had escaped one danger only to fall into another. They were lost in an immense wilderness and did not know where to turn.

The locomotive finally succeeded in climbing a tall tree, and made out smoke rising in the distance.

To this, they painfully made their way and, after a terrible struggle, came to an old saw-mill by the side of a little stream. It was a hideous old mill, of a villainous aspect that alarmed them both. But here was their only hope, and so the two unfortunate machines found them-

selves obliged to apply to the mill for shelter and fuel.

The mill welcomed them very hospitably, but there was something in his dusty, oily manner that the locomotive did not trust, and he resolved to stay awake and watch. The little delicate steamboat was, by this time, too exhausted to notice anything. After they had drunk many barrels of water each, they revived a little, and the mill offered them a few tons of sawdust, which, he said, was the only fuel he could give them. At the first trial the steamer whispered to the locomotive that it tasted queerly, but they decided it was only the oil in which it was soaked. At any rate they had to eat that or nothing, and they made a meal of it without more ado.

Hardly had they burned the last mouthful before they fell into a heavy sleep and knew nothing for many hours. The locomotive was awakened by a sudden pain, and he was terrified to find the teeth of a buzz-saw cutting through his side. He sprang up with a roar, but it was too late, his left side wheel had been bitten off! He charged furiously at the sides of the mill and tore open a great hole, then dragged out the steamboat, and ran her into the forest as fast as his five wheels could carry him.

As they stood trembling in the forest, a sudden glare of light attracted their attention. The mill was on fire, set, no doubt, from some sparks dropped by the locomotive in its terrible struggle for escape. By the light of the burning mill, they made their way through the forest. With new fuel and water, their strength had been partially renewed and terror increased their efforts.

In the morning, after a short sleep, they awoke to find themselves by the side of a wide river to which they had hobbled during the night, but had not seen in the dark. Alongside the bank of the stream ran a beautiful level railway line. They looked and looked, hardly able to believe their windows. It was too good to be true!

It did not take them long to decide what to do. The little steamboat gave one leap into the river and whistled long and merrily. The locomotive crawled onto the line, and rang its bell in a joyous peal. For they knew, by the looks of the country, that they had been travelling in a huge semi-circle and that the river and the railway led directly into the City o' Ligg.

So they steamed along, side by side, the lame locomotive and the sorrowful, shamefaced steamboat. That day one laid her head at last alongside the dock, and one puffed timidly into the station; both decided never to complain of any work that they should have to do in the future.

Little Gulliver*

LOUISA M. ALCOTT

UP IN the lighthouse lived Davy with Old Dan, the keeper. Most boys would have found it very lonely; but Davy had three friends, and was as happy as the day was long. One of Davy's friends was the great lamp, which was lighted at sunset and burned all night, to guide the ships into the harbor. To Dan it was only a lamp; but, to the boy, it seemed a living thing, and he loved and tended it faithfully. Every day he helped clean the big wick, polish the brass work, and wash the glass lantern which protected the flame. Every evening he went up to see it lighted and always fell asleep thinking, "No matter how dark the night, my good Shine will save the ships."

Davy's second friend was Nep, the Newfoundland, who was washed ashore from a wreck and who had never left the island since. Nep was rough and big, but no one could look in his soft, brown eyes and not trust him. He

*From *Aunt Jo's Scrap Bag*. Used by permission of the publishers, Little, Brown & Co.

followed Davy's steps all day, slept at his feet all night, and more than once had saved his life when Davy fell among the rocks, or got caught by the rising tide.

But the dearest friend of all was a sea gull. Davy found him with a broken wing, and nursed him till he was well. He was very fond of "Little Gulliver," as he called him. The bird came daily to talk with him, telling wild stories about his wanderings by land and sea.

Old Dan was Davy's uncle—a grim, gray man, who said little, did his work faithfully, and was both father and mother to Davy, who had no parents and no friends beyond the island. That was his world; and he led a quiet life among his playfellows, the wind and waves. He seldom went to the mainland, three miles away, for he was happier at home. He watched the sea anemones open below the water, found curious and pretty shells, and sometimes more valuable treasures washed up from some wreck. He saw little, yellow crabs and ugly lobsters. Sometimes a whale or a shark swam by, and often sleek, black seals came up to bask on the rocks. He gathered sea-weeds, from tiny red cobwebs to great scalloped leaves of kelp, longer than himself. He heard the waves dash and roar, the winds howl or sigh, and the gulls scream shrilly as they dipped and dived, or sailed away to follow the ships that came and went from all parts of the world.

With Nep and Gulliver, he roamed about his small kingdom; or, if storms raged, he sat up in the tower, safe and dry, watching the tumult of sea and sky. He never was afraid for Nep nestled at his feet, Dan sat close by, and overhead the great lamp shone far out into the night.

Close by the tower hung the fog bell, which would ring all night. One day Dan found that something among the chains was broken; and, having vainly tried to mend it, he decided to go to town and get what was needed.

"A heavy fog is blowing up and I must be off at once. I shall be back before dark," said Dan.

Away went the little boat; the fog shut down over it, as if a misty wall had parted Davy from his uncle. He sat and read for an hour, then fell asleep and forgot everything till Nep's cold nose on his hand waked him up. It was nearly dark; and, hoping to find Dan had come, he ran down to the landing-place. But no boat was there, and the fog was thicker than ever. Dan never had been gone so long before, and Davy was afraid something had happened to him. Then he cheered up and took courage.

"It is sunset by the clock; so I'll light the lamp, and, if Dan is lost in the fog, it will guide him home," said Davy.

Up he went, and soon the great star shown out above the black-topped lighthouse, glimmering through the fog, as if eager to be seen. Davy had his supper, but no Dan came. The fog thickened, the lamp was hardly seen, and no bell rang to warn the ships of the dangerous rocks. Poor Davy could not sleep, but all night long wandered from the tower to the door watching, calling, and wondering. At sunrise he put out the light, ate a little breakfast, and roved about the island hoping to see some sign of

Dan. The sun drew up the fog at last, and he could see the blue bay, the distant town, and a few fishing boats going out to sea. But nowhere was the island boat with gray Old Dan in it. Davy's heart grew heavier and heavier. In the afternoon Gulliver appeared. To him Davy told his trouble, and the three friends took counsel together.

"I've howled all day, hoping some one would hear me, but no one does and I'm discouraged," said Nep.

"I'll fly to town and try to learn what has become of Dan. Then I'll come and tell you. Cheer up, Davy. I'll bring you tidings!" With these cheerful words, away sailed Gulliver, leaving his master to watch and wait again.

The broken wing was not quite well, else Gulliver would have been able to steer clear of a boat that came swiftly by. A sudden gust drove the gull so violently against the sail that he dropped breathless into the boat, and a little girl caught him before he could recover himself. "Oh, what a lovely bird! I wanted a gull, and I'll keep this one."

Poor Gulliver struggled, pecked and screamed; but Dora held him fast, and shut him in a basket till they reached the shore. Then she put him in a lobster pot—a large wooden thing, something like a cage—and left him on the lawn where he could catch glimpses of the sea and watch the lighthouse tower, as he sat alone. For three long days and nights he was a prisoner, and suffered much. Boys poked and pulled him; little girls admired him. Cats prowled about his cage; dogs barked at him; hens cackled over him; and a shrill canary jeered at him from its pretty pagoda. Through the stillness of the night, he heard the waves break on the shore; the wind came singing up from the sea; the moon shone. But no one spoke a friendly word to him, and he pined away with a broken heart. On the fourth night, little Gulliver saw a black shadow steal across the lawn and heard a soft voice say:

"Poor bird, I'se gwine to let yer go. Specs little missy'll scold dreffle; jes wait till I gits de knots out of de string dat ties de door, and away you flies. You's a slave, like I was once; and it's a dreffle hard ting, I knows. I got away, and I means you shall."

"Do you live here? I never saw you playing with the other children," said the gull.

"Yes, I lives here, and helps de cook. You didn't see me, kase I never plays, de chil'en don't like me."

"Why not?" asked Gulliver, wondering.

"I'se black," said Moppet, with a sob.

"But that's silly," cried the bird. "The peeps are gray, the seals black, and the crabs yellow, but we are all friends."

"Nobody in de world keres for me." The black eyes grew so dim with tears that the poor child couldn't see that the last knot was out. Gulliver saw it, and, pushing up the door, flew from his prison with a glad cry.

"I wish you could go and live with Davy," whispered Gulliver. He told her all his story, and they agreed that he should fly to the island, and see if Dan was there. If not, he was to come back and Moppet would try to get someone to help find him. Full of hope and joy, Gulliver spread his wings; but alas, he was too weak to fly. For three days he had sat moping in the cage till his strength was gone.

"What shall I do?" he cried fluttering his feeble wings.

"I knows a little cove down yonder, where no one goes; and dere you kin stay till you's better. I'll come and feed you." As Moppet spoke, she took Gulliver in her arms and stole down to the lonely spot where nothing went but the winds and waves, the gulls, and little Moppet. Here she left the bird, and, with a loving "good-night," crept home to her bed in the garret, feeling rich as a queen.

Next day, a great storm came. The wind blew a hurricane, the rain poured, and the sea thundered on the coast. Gulliver spent an anxious day, sitting in a cranny of the rock, thinking of Davy and Moppet. At nightfall the storm raged fiercer than ever, and he gave up seeing Moppet for he was sure she wouldn't come through the pelting rain to feed him. But a voice cried through the darkness: "Is you dere, honey?" and Moppet came climbing over the rocks with a basket full of such bits as she could get.

"It's so stormy, I can't get to Davy; and I worry about him," began Gulliver. But, suddenly, a faint sound came up from below, as if someone called, "Help, help!"

"Hi! what's dat?" said Moppet, listening.

"Davy, Davy!" called the voice.

"It's Dan. Hurrah, we've found him!" Gulliver dived off the rocks so recklessly that he went splash into the water, but that didn't matter to him. Down by the seaside lay Dan, so bruised he couldn't move and so

faint with hunger he could hardly speak. As soon as
Gulliver called, Moppet scrambled down and fed the poor
man with her scraps, brought him rainwater from a nearby
crevice and bound his wounded head with her apron. Then
Dan told them how his boat had been run down by a ship
in the fog; how he was cast ashore in the lonely cove; how
he had lain there; how the sound of Moppet's voice told
him that help was near. How glad they all were! Moppet
danced for joy. Gulliver screamed and flapped his wings.

"What will Davy do? He may try to come ashore. Is
the lamp alight?" cried Dan.

Gulliver flew up to the highest rock, and looked out
across the dark sea. Yes, there it was, the steady star
shining through the storm and saying plainly, "All is well."

"Thank heaven! If the lamp is burning, Davy is alive!
Now, how shall I get to him?" said Dan.

"Never you fret, massa. Dere's folks in de house as'll
tend to you, ef I tells 'em where you is."

Off she ran and soon came back with help. Dan was taken to the house and carefully tended.

In the morning, Gulliver flew to the tower where Davy still watched and waited. He told his adventures, while Davy laughed and cried, and Nep wagged his tail for joy. Then came a boat to carry Davy ashore, while another keeper took charge of the light till Dan was well.

While Dan lay sick, Moppet tended him like a loving little daughter; and, when he was well, he took her for his own. It was a happy day when Dan and Davy, Moppet, Gulliver, and Nep sailed away to the island. The sun was setting, and they floated through waves as rosy as the rosy sky. A fresh wind filled the sail, and Gulliver sat on the masthead. Dan held the tiller and Davy lay at his feet, with Nep bolt upright beside him, but the happiest face of all was Moppet's. Kneeling at the bow, she leaned forward. Like a little black figurehead of Hope, she looked, as the boat flew on, bearing her away from the old life into the new.

As the sun sank, out shone the lamp with sudden brightness, as if the island bade them welcome. Dan furled the sail; and, drifting with the tide, they floated in, till the waves broke softly on the shore and left them safe at home.

THE SEA GULL

MARY HOWITT

OH, the white Sea gull, the wild Sea gull,
  A joyful bird is he,
As he lies like a cradled thing at rest
In the arms of a sunny sea!
The little waves rock to and fro,
And the white gull lies asleep,
As the fisher's bark, with breeze and tide,
Goes merrily over the deep!

The ship, with her fair sails set, goes by,
And her people stand to note
How the Sea gull sits on the rocking waves,
As if in an anchored boat.
The sea is fresh, the sea is fair,
And the sky calm overhead,
And the Sea gull lies on the deep, deep sea,
Like a king in his royal bed.

ALL ABOUT COLUMBUS

COLUMBUS sailed the ocean blue
In fourteen-hundred-ninety-two.

He said: "I think the earth is round,
And I'll sail round it, I'll be bound!"
But the wise men said: "The earth is flat,
You'll fall off the edge if you sail like that,

You'll meet strange monsters in the sea,
And what a calamity that would be!"
But Columbus sailed and he sailed some more,
Till at last he found America's shore!

IN COLUMBUS' TIME*

SUPPOSE you lived then, do you think that you
Would believe what Columbus said was true
Or would you be like the wise men who
Laughed in his face and said, "Pooh, pooh?"
—*Annette Wynne*

*Taken from *For Days and Days*, by the kind permission of Frederick A. Stokes Company.

112

The First Thanksgiving Day

Olive Beaupré Miller

LONG ago the little band of Pilgrims—50 men, 20 women and 34 children—left England on the ship *Mayflower*. Turning their backs on the Old World, they headed over stormy seas for the New World. There they meant to build a homeland, where they could be free, where there were no kings to oppress them, and where they would not be thrown into prison or otherwise punished if their way of worshiping God was different from that of the rulers of the land.

In the cold of November, 1620, they reached Massachusetts and went ashore to build their homes at Plymouth. There they were in the New World at last—old Elder Brewster, their leader; pretty Priscilla Mulleins; fiery little Captain Standish, and all the rest.

DOROTHY TODD

Around them the land was a wilderness, inhabited only by Indians, and before they could get more than the rudest shelters up, the snows began. Never in England had the Pilgrims seen such heavy snows or suffered cold so severe. And they did not have enough to eat. When they first left England they had had another ship, the *Speedwell,* with them. She had carried Pilgrims who had been living in Holland to escape the wrath of King James of England. But twice the *Speedwell* had sprung leaks at sea, forcing them to return to England. There they had finally abandoned her. All of them had crowded on the *Mayflower.* Thus they were obliged to live on such food as that one ship could carry.

So many mouths to feed! And so little with which to feed them!

Through that long hard winter, when everyone was half frozen and half starved, the
women gave much of their own food to the
children. So the children fared better than
their parents. There was much sickness in
the village and many people died.

Then at last the first little buds appeared
on trees and bushes and the grass in the
meadows turned green. How the Pilgrims
rejoiced! They could plant crops and raise food! Men, women, and
children went to work, helped by the Indian, Squanto, who had become
their friend. Squanto had been to England, he spoke English very well,
and now he taught them how to raise corn, an American plant unknown
in England. They built seven homes and four buildings for common
use. And they had made friends with the neighboring Indians.

When the huge, powerful chief, Massasoit, first appeared at Plymouth with his band of fiercely painted braves, there had been great
fear in the village. Boldly little Captain Standish had gone to meet
him, though the big chief towered nearly three heads taller than he.
But there had been no need for Standish to use the muskets of his little
army, for gifts and kindly words, spoken by leading Pilgrims and in-
terpreted by Squanto, had made Massasoit their friend.

"Now," they said, "we walk as peaceably and safely in the woods
about Plymouth as we did on the highways in England."

When they gathered their first harvest it was scanty. Though their
corn had done well, thanks to Squanto, their barley, wheat and peas
had come to almost nothing. But after their terrible winter they were
so grateful for what they had now that they decided to celebrate with
a day of thanksgiving to God, who had brought them to this Land of
Promise and with His goodness, sustained them there. So the men
went out to shoot wild turkeys, waterfowl, and deer. And they invited
Massasoit to their feast. When he arrived he had ninety hungry braves
with him! But they were welcomed. It was a golden day in Indian

Summer, corn stood stacked in the little fields and among the stacks were big yellow pumpkins, such as the Indians grew. Joyously, Indians and Pilgrims sat down to eat together.

The table was loaded with good things—venison, roast duck, roast goose, white bread, corn bread, berries and wild plums. But best of all were the delicious roast turkeys. Never had the Pilgrims tasted turkey in England, for turkeys, like corn and pumpkins, were native to America, where they lived, wild, in the woods. Before they ate, Governor Bradford rose and spoke out of a full heart. He thanked God, he praised God. And men, women and children felt as deeply thankful as he. They thanked God, they praised God, but not only for the harvest, as men had done in other harvest festivals in the world. They thanked God because God had led them, as He once led the Children of Israel, out of a land where they were oppressed to a land where they could be free and order their lives as they chose.

After that the Pilgrims and their Indian guests began to eat. With much talk and laughter, they ate until they could eat no more.

Then Captain Standish, wearing his shiny steel helmet and corselet and flourishing his sword, put his little army through a military drill. He had no more than twenty men and they were awkward enough, having never been trained as soldiers. But they had rigged themselves up with any bit of military finery they could find and they had proved often enough that they knew how to use their muskets. So even though they didn't all hold their muskets at the same angle or move together and in the right direction at the very instant the Captain gave a command, they presented an imposing appearance.

When the drill was over, there were games of skill—foot races, high jumps, long jumps. The moon was well up in the sky before the festival ended. Then the Indians went off to sleep in the woods and the Pilgrims retired to their homes.

Such was the first American Thanksgiving Day, a day of great joy after a time of much suffering and sorrow, a day of dwelling on the good that had been received, a day of true thanksgiving to God.

GIVE PRAISE

Heap high the board with plenteous cheer
     and gather to the feast,
And toast that sturdy Pilgrim band
     whose courage never ceased.
Give praise to that All Gracious One
     by whom their steps were led,
And thanks unto the harvest's Lord
     who sends our "daily bread."

From The First Thanksgiving Day
by Alice Williams Brotherton

WE THANK THEE

RALPH WALDO EMERSON

FOR flowers that bloom about our feet;
  FOR tender grass, so fresh, so sweet;
For song of bird, and hum of bee;
For all things fair we hear or see,
     Father in heaven, we thank Thee!
For blue of stream and blue of sky;
For pleasant shade of branches high;
For fragrant air and cooling breeze;
For beauty of the blooming trees,
     Father in heaven, we thank Thee!

George Washington and the First American Flag

IN a beautiful, big white house high above the Potomac River in Virginia, George Washington, a kindly country gentleman, lived with Martha, his wife, and Martha's two jolly children, Jack and Patsey Custis. There were plenty of dogs and horses around the big estate. There were beautiful gardens also; and from the fine green lawn there was a splendid view over the Potomac River. Life was very happy in that pleasant, spacious home until sad times came for the country Washington loved so well.

This picture of Washington, riding around his estate at Mt. Vernon, and the one on page 119, are from Currier and Ives prints.

In those days there was no United States at all. There were thirteen little colonies along the Atlantic Ocean where the people were chiefly farmers, living in plain little houses. These colonies had been settled by men and women from Europe, who had left the Old World because they wanted to be free of kings and other harsh rulers.

In old-fashioned sailing vessels, they had crossed endless miles of a stormy, wind-swept ocean. Arriving in the New World with little they could call their own, they had found before them a wilderness, a land of unploughed soil and age-old forests through which the Indians slipped on their silent, moccasined feet. But they had hewed the great trees

From 1835-1895, these popular Currier and Ives prints, found in many American homes, recorded the history, customs, and life of the United States.

in the forests, cleared the land, ploughed and planted it, fighting the Indians when they chanced to be attacked. Thus, with unending toil, they had turned the wilderness into prosperous farms, trying to make little homes for their swarming families of children. But though these people had come from many different countries in Europe, the land now belonged to the King of England. And this King, living so far away across the ocean, knew little of what was needed in a land he had never seen and in which he had little interest.

In fact, George III of England cared nothing about what was needed anywhere in his realm. What he wanted was money to spend and little did he care whether the means he took to get money out of his subjects were just or unjust, right or wrong. "Be a King, George!" the King's mother had said to him when he was only a boy and George had grown up to believe that the only way to be a king was to make others do what he willed, whether they liked or no. Many people in England thought the King willful and headstrong, but there they could elect men to speak for them in Parliament and keep the King under control.

In America it was different. The toiling American farmers, in their little, checkered, green fields so newly carved from the wilderness, were not allowed to send men to Parliament to stand up for them to the King. The colonies were to George III nothing more than districts where he could get money easily without running any risk of having men talk back and balk him in his plans. Year after year, the wrongs he did the American colonists continued to grow greater until at last there was nothing that men of spirit could do but stand up and fight for their rights.

It was a sad day for George Washington when he knew that this was true; for George still loved the old England from which his forefathers had come. He loved his family, too, and the beautiful country estate he was now obliged to leave. But he could not see great wrongs done and do nothing to set them right. Those strong men, who had faced all the dangers and difficulties of building homes in a wilderness, had dreamed that their labor was building a land where men should be free—not borne down and oppressed as they had been back in Europe. And now that great dream was in danger. The American dream of freedom for men and women to work with equal opportunity to better themselves in life was in danger of dying out before it had well begun. So Washington kissed his wife good-bye. His family and his servants waved their last farewells from the lawn of lovely Mt. Vernon and he rode off to join the soldiers.

Years ago, when Washington was little more than a boy, he had fought against the Indians out on the western frontier; so he not only knew how to fight, but, more important still, he knew how to lead other men. Among all the leaders who gathered in Philadelphia to help the American people, Washington was the greatest. Hence he was appointed by the Congress of the Colonies to be the commander-in-chief of the new American army.

Raw, awkward farmers they were, with little training in warfare. Leaving their ploughs, they took their guns and came to fight. Sleek in their splendid uniforms, the scarlet-coated soldiers who served King George III laughed at these ungainly farmers; yet under Washington's leadership they became well-trained troops in time. With courage they stood up under fire against the soldiers of the King. Sometimes they lost a battle, and sometimes they won a great victory. But, whichever way their fortunes went, Washington kept them together, fighting for their freedom. His stepson, Jack Custis, was now old enough to be with him sometimes in campaigns, but the heart of the General never ceased to long for lovely Mt. Vernon.

On the Fourth of July in 1776 the Continental Congress declared that the American colonies were henceforth independent of the mother country, England. Thus a very

This picture is from the painting, *The Declaration of Independence*, painted in 1816, by John Trumbull, a famous American painter of the time. It is in the Capitol, at Washington.

young, new nation was born to the family of nations—a youthful United States, awkward and clumsy yet as an overgrown country boy, but as full of promise, too, as lusty and as strong. In its Declaration of Independence, the United States had declared that all men are created free and equal.

Then men and women began to say in the crooked little streets of Boston, on the water front in New York, among the prim, red-brick houses of Quaker Philadelphia, and through all the farms of the country: "We want a flag of our own. We have hauled down the flag of old England and we need a new banner to follow, a new sign of our union to stand before the world."

Now Washington had heard of a woman named Betsy Ross, who lived in Philadelphia. "The finest needlewoman in America," Betsy Ross was called. There was just the woman to make a new flag for the country. So one fine day in June George Washington walked with two friends through the pleasant streets of the quaint, old Quaker city.

In answer to his knock at the door of a trim red-brick house, Betsy Ross herself appeared, followed by her black cat, Powder and when she saw General Washington she hastened to drop a curtsy.

"A fine day, Mistress Ross!" Washington said. "We come to you on important business."

"You're very welcome, sir!" Betsy bobbed another curtsy. Then she led the men into the house and into her little back parlor. "Now, sir, what can I do for you?" She was eager to know their errand.

The General answered her smiling: "Congress has just accepted a design for our new flag and so we've come to you, ma'am, to ask you to make it for us!"

Betsy beamed with pleasure. "I'll try my best," she said.

Then the General produced a paper on which was a drawing. "See," he said, "there are to be thirteen stripes, seven red ones and six white ones—one stripe for each of the colonies. And in the upper left-hand corner there will be a blue field with a circle of thirteen white stars—one for each of our colonies which have now become states in our Union."

Betsy studies the drawing with interest.

"It's a beautiful design," she said, "but why have the stars six points? I see no reason for that."

Washington heaved a gentle sigh. "The stars we have known so long on shields and coats-of-arms in England are always made with six points." He liked the star that reminded him of his family's homeland across the sea.

OVER THE HILLS

"If six-pointed stars are English, all the more reason why ours should be different!" Betsy cried with spirit. "Here in our new world we want to start life afresh. We must look at things through our own eyes, not through the eyes of our forefathers who lived long ago in England. Look up at the stars some night! You'll see they have only five points! If we're going to face life truly in this new country of ours, wouldn't it be better to place on our flag the stars just as we really see them, rather than as men have drawn them for so many ages past?"

General Washington's face was grave.

"I doubt very much," he said, trying to find an excuse, "if you'll be able to cut a perfect five-pointed star."

Betsy seized a piece of paper, folded it, snipped with her scissors, opened the paper again and triumphantly held up to view a perfect five-pointed star!

The men with Washington smiled. "You're defeated, General!" they cried and even Powder, the cat, appeared to smile his approval.

An answering smile lit the face of General Washington. "So be it!" he agreed. "America's star shall be hers alone! God grant it may guide her to realize her dream!"

Thus it was that Betsy Ross made the first flag of the United States, the first Stars and Stripes! Hard were the battles Washington fought for several years after that, with the Stars and Stripes as his banner. Many were the dark days and the hardships he endured from the freezing Christmas night, when he crossed the Delaware River through the churning cakes of ice, to the terrible winter at Valley Forge, when his men were ragged and starving.

While Charles Peale and Gilbert Stuart were painting Washington in the European manner, American sign painters and home folks were painting him in their own purely American way. This 18th-century picture of Washington directing a battle came from a Massachusetts tavern.

But in time, the day of victory came when all the English King's troops had to leave American shores, and the new United States was at last free to thrive and grow. But then there remained for George Washington an even harder task. Not yet could he go back to live at his lovely Mt. Vernon, for he was elected first president of this young and sprawling republic. It was he who must keep the thirteen young states together and lay the foundations for a government which he hoped, in time, would make real that great American dream of equal opportunities for all men and women to work and be justly rewarded for their work.

When Washington was finally free to go back home to Mt. Vernon, two more children, George Washington Parke

Custis and Eleanor Parke Custis, the son and daughter of Jack Custis, brought life and laughter again into the big white house on the green lawns above the Potomac. There, as a country gentleman, Washington spent his last days.

From the time of George Washington on, except for one short period,* the stripes on the American flag have remained thirteen in number, to remind men of those original thirteen plucky little colonies who first fought so staunchly for freedom. But, as the adventurous American pioneers pushed west on foot or horseback or in great covered wagons as far as the Mississippi and west again to the Rockies and west to the far Pacific, swarming over the breadth of the continent, many new states were formed. And, as each new state joined the Union, a new five-pointed star was added to the field of blue. Today, there are fifty stars representing the fifty great states, which Americans won by toil in their battles with the wilderness. So today when the flag goes by, we remember all of this; but we think with deep feeling, too, of the more important fact that the Stars and Stripes were meant to stand in the hearts of Americans for the great American dream—the great American hope of a better world for all!

*In May, 1795, Congress passed a law authorizing 15 stars and 15 stripes to include new states, Vermont and Kentucky, and the addition of a star and stripe for each future state admitted. But in 1818, another law was passed providing for the addition of a star for each new state, but reducing the number of stripes to the original thirteen.

The Fourth of July

OLIVE BEAUPRÉ MILLER

HAIL Columbia, happy land!
The band plays in the park,
And crowds of people everywhere
Are laughing in the dark.

Stars from Roman candles pop;
Pinwheels whirl in flame;
Huge and fiery letters write
George Washington's great name.

Siss, boom, bah! A golden snake,
Against the black of night,
Shoots up and up and up, and bursts
To shower bouquets of light!

Hurrah for Independence Day!
Hurrah for the Fourth of July!
When rockets write the people's joy
In flames across the sky!

THE YANKEE PEDDLER

Olive Beaupré Miller

The peddler rode up hill and down,
He drove his horse from town to town,
He took his wonderful traveling store
Right straight up to a farmer's door.

"Come buy! Come buy! Come buy!" he'd shout,
Then everyone came rushing out
To see what he'd brought from far away,
To ask him all the news of the day.

No railroads crossed the country then,
No radio flashed the news to men,
And Indians still lurked in the woods
When the Yankee peddler came west with his goods.

From the East to the lonely West he'd go,
And he'd tell all the news people wanted to know.
They even asked in towns where he went
Who'd been elected President.

His big red wagon was tightly packed
With things people wanted, things they lacked.
No wonder lonesome settlers ran out
As soon as they heard the peddler's shout.

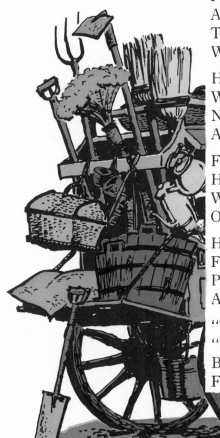

For men he had axes, shovels, spades,
Hoes and knives with strong steel blades.
Women he'd tempt with a fine display
Of colorful dress goods, bright and gay.

He carried baskets, tubs and brooms,
Feather dusters for dusting rooms,
Pots for coffee, pots for tea,
And everything else one could wish to see.

"That beautiful clock!" a woman would sigh,
"If I had the money, that's what I'd buy;
But I'll have to buy a brush and a tub,
For I've clothes to wash and floors to scrub!"

A boy, with hard-earned pennies, took
What he most wanted—a book! A book!
He'd sink himself in a story then
And never look up from his book again.

A coffee grinder charmed a girl—
Laughing, she'd give its handle a twirl,
She'd grind that handle round and round,
As though she had coffee to be ground.

All was excitement, everyone talked,
Even the chickens ran up and squawked.
What a day for them all! What a day! What a day!
When the Yankee peddler came their way!

ABRAHAM LINCOLN*

1809-1865

ROSEMARY AND STEPHEN VINCENT BENÉT

LINCOLN was a long man.
He liked out of doors.
He liked the wind blowing
And the talk in country stores.

He liked telling stories,
He liked telling jokes.
"Abe's quite a character,"
Said quite a lot of folks.

Lots of folks in Springfield
Saw him every day,
Walking down the street
In his gaunt, long way.

Shawl around his shoulders,
Letters in his hat.
"That's Abe Lincoln,"
They thought no more than that.

HERBERT
RUDEEN

*From *A Book of Americans*, published by Farrar & Rinehart, Inc. Copyright, 1933, by Rosemary and Stephen Vincent Benet.

132

OVER THE HILLS

A Story About Abe Lincoln

ABE Lincoln was born in a one-room log cabin in
Kentucky. Dennis Hanks, his cousin, used to tell
how he ran hotfoot as a boy to see that new baby as soon
as he heard Abe was born. He found the baby and its
mother lying under a bearskin in a rude bed made of
logs. And so interested was he in this squirming bit of
new life that he stayed all night in the cabin, sleeping
on the floor. In the morning he insisted on holding Abe
in his arms. But the baby screwed up its face and cried
without letup. Passing Abe to an aunt, Dennis said
in disgust:

"Take him! He'll never grow up to be much!"

When Abe was eight, Thomas Lincoln, his father,
moved the family to Indiana. Young though he was, Abe
was already able to swing an axe like a man. He helped
his father cut down trees and build the new log cabin.
But between spells of work, Nancy Lincoln, his mother,
scrubbed his face and sent him off to school.

"Abe, you go to school and larn all you kin," she said.

So Abe trudged off through the woods. Eighteen miles he walked every day to and from the nearest log school-house. How that boy wanted to learn! Stretched on the floor by the fireplace, he read late every night. Cousin Dennis scoffed at him. "Abe's peculiarsome," he said. For wildcats were then more plentiful than books in Indiana.

Abe shot up like green corn, tall and lean and lanky. At nineteen he was running a flatboat loaded with grain and pork down the Mississippi to New Orleans.

Borne downstream by the river, Abe's flatboat had no motive power of its own. Steered by a great oar at its stern, it floated along amid a crowd of other boats and rafts. Often those rafts bore small log cabins and a whole family on its way to settle in the West. Men steered the rafts, women worked at washtubs, and children played about among chickens, pigs and a cow or two. Abe had

to watch out lest his boat be grounded on a sandbar or flung ashore by crazily changing currents. And he had to be on guard a-gainst river pirates who tricked boatmen into landing near their hang-out at Cave-in-Rock, Illi-nois, then murdered them and stole their boats.

On one of Abe's trips his boat got stuck on a mill dam in the Sanga-mon River below the

hill-town of New Salem, Illinois. All the townsfolk watched him get his boat afloat and Abe liked them so much that he returned to settle there. But the Sangamon River Boys, meaning to test him, said, "You can't settle here until you've raced our fastest runner, thrown our champion wrestler and fought our best fist fighter."

"Trot 'em out," Abe said. The race he won easily. And when the huge wrestler rushed at him like a battering ram, Abe dodged aside, caught him by the nape of the neck and threw him heels over head. Then he shouted, "Bring on your next man!"

But the boys had seen enough. We'll take you in," they said. So Abe settled in New Salem, clerking in a store and studying law by candlelight at night.

The upper pictures show New Salem as it has been rebuilt and may be seen today.

Soon he had a store of his own. But business was poor so he had to sell it. Then the men who bought it ran away without paying for it. Left with a big pile of debts, Abe husked corn and split fence rails to pay his debts. But his troubles didn't keep him from seeing that a boy chopping wood in the snow, with rags tied around his feet, got a pair of shoes. The Sangamon River Boys were now his fast friends. Working with other friends, won by Abe's honesty and kindness, they elected him to represent them in the Illinois State Legislature.

So Abe went to Springfield, the capital of the State. There he practiced law along with his other duties. But he was never too busy to be kind. One day after a rainstorm he rode down a country lane with three other lawyers. They were hurrying to court to speak at a trial before a judge, a jury and the lawyers who would oppose them. But as they rode along, Abe saw two robins fluttering in great distress in a tree above him.

"What's the matter with those robins?" Abe drew up his horse. Then he heard a faint chirping in the grass beside him. "The storm must have blown their little ones from the nest," he said. "What a pity! Those little birds will starve if they're not put back in the nest!"

"What's the difference if they do starve?" one of the lawyers cried impatiently. "Two less robins won't be missed in the world! Come on or we'll be late for court!"

Then he and the other two men rode off. But Abe stayed behind. Of course it was only a robin family which had fallen into difficulties. But Mr. and Mrs.

Robin were so worried about it and the little robins were surely in great distress. Their chirping was growing fainter though one of them now and then managed to give a sharp little screech.

Down from his horse sprang Abe. In the long grass he searched while the parent robins eyed him anxiously. The little ones were so tiny, it took Abe some minutes to find them. But when he came on them, so awkward, forlorn and ugly in their few straggly feathers, he picked them up very gently and held them in his hand. Then he looked about to discover where their nest might be. In a moment more he spied it. It was high up in the tree. He would have to climb the tree to reach it. That wasn't good for a man all dressed in his Sunday-best clothes, ready to appear in a law court and hoping to make an impression, not only on a dignified judge, but also on the members of the jury and the lawyers pitted against him. But still, what must be must be! Who could let little birds starve? Quickly Abe climbed the tree regardless of what might happen to his Sunday clothes.

He laid the two little birds gently in their nest. Cozily they cuddled down while their mother and father hovered in great satisfaction above. Then off went Abe at full gallop, hurrying on to court.

When birds or people were miserable Abe just had to help them. On his trips down the Mississippi he had seen Negro slaves bought and sold like cattle. Surely that wasn't right! He began to talk about letting no new states come into the Union as slave states. And while men argued this question hotly, with many ready to fight about it, Abe kept on talking until the whole country heard about him. At last, despite Cousin Dennis's belief that Abe would never grow up to be much, he was elected President and went with his wife and sons to live in the White House. Then in the midst of war, he set the Negroes free. For all his life long Abe remained the same man who had risked spoiling his Sunday clothes and being late for court rather than leave two helpless little birds to starve to death.

This picture of the Lincoln family in the White House, made by an artist of the time, snows President and Mrs. Lincoln with their sons, Robert, Thomas and William.

John Henry, the Big Steel-Drivin' Man

FROM AMERICAN POPULAR BALLADS

HAMMERING steel spikes down to keep railroad rails in place was no easy job. But John Henry, the giant Negro, could do it better than any other man. Then the Chesapeake and Ohio Railroad decided to cut the Big Bend Tunnel through the mountains of West Virginia. And driving spikes to make holes for the blasts of dynamite that blew out the rock for the tunnel was an even more difficult job. But that didn't bother John Henry. Off he went with his pretty little wife, Polly Ann, and their children, a boy and a girl, to the shanty town for workmen beside the Big Bend Tunnel. Seeking the foreman, he said he wanted a job. Then he started to sing—

"When John Henry was a very small boy,
A-holdin' to his mama's hand,
He said: 'If I live until I'm twenty-one,
I'm goin' to be a steel-drivin' man!'"

But the foreman said nothing.
So John Henry sang on—

"Captain, I'm a steel-drivin' man,
I can drive more steel than any other man!
I'll die with my hammer in my hand, Lord, Lord!
I'll die with my hammer in my hand!"

Then the foreman had to smile and he said:
"Well, if you're that good, I'll give you a job!"

So John Henry went
to work in the tunnel. And Polly Ann cleaned up
one of the shanties for their home while the children
raced around, gathered wild flowers and made merry.
No such steel driver as John Henry had the workmen
ever seen. Every time he swung his hammer he drove the
spike an inch down into the rock. And the boy who knelt
on the ground, holding the spike in place could always be
sure it would be the spike and not his head that John Henry
would hit. Daily John Henry's fame as the champion
steel driver grew. And Polly Ann was almost as famous as
he. Once when John Henry was sick, Polly Ann took his
hammer and drove spikes in his stead. All the men cheered
her. One and all, they sang—

> *"John Henry had a pretty little wife,*
> *Her name was Polly Ann.*
> *John Henry got sick and had to go to bed,*
> *Polly Ann drove steel like a man!"*

Thus everything went well until one night the foreman
gathered all the workmen together and said:

"Men, an engine has been invented which drives the
drills by steam. It can work faster than any man. Soon
we'll have one here in Big Bend!"

Then all the men were sad. For if the machine could do their work, they wouldn't have jobs any more nor food for their wives and children. But now John Henry cried:

"I'll race that steam drill! I'll beat it! I'll show that a man's a man.—Lord, Lord, Oh Lord! I'll prove that the man you made is better'n any man-made machine!"

At that the steel drivers took heart. But Polly Ann and the children began to worry. And Polly Ann reminded John Henry how he used to sing a song that went—

"When John Henry was seven years old,
A-sittin' on his father's knee,
He said, 'The Big Bend Tunnel
on the C and O Road
Is goin' to be the death of me!'"

And John Henry's little boy climbed on his knee and said:

"Oh, Papa, if you beat that steam drill down you'll die with your hammer in your hand!"

But John Henry wouldn't listen to them.

In time the great day came. A big crowd gathered in the tunnel. John Henry stood on the right side with the big steam drill on the left. And he said, "Before I let that steam drill beat me down I'll hammer my fool self to death!" Then he turned to the boy who held his spike and cried, "Big boy, you'd better pray, for if I miss this piece of steel, tomorrow'll be your buryin' day!"

At that he lifted his hammer and the foreman gave the signal to start. With a ring like silver John Henry's hammer came down on the great steel spike. An inch and a half he drove it into the rock. But the steam engine chugged and started its drill to whirring. Whirring, purring, rasping, clanging, that steam drill made a terrible noise very different from the silver ring of John Henry's hammer. Yet never for an instant did it let up driving. It had no arm to lift, as John Henry had. It just bored on and on. Faster and faster John Henry swung his arm till the ring of his hammer seemed to come with a constant singing and the tremendous force of his blows splitting the solid rock made a sound as though the whole mountain were cracking.

All day and all night John Henry swung his hammer. And at daybreak he said, "I can feel my muscles givin' way!" But still he pounded and pounded. It was ten o'clock when the foreman cried, "Time's up! Stop drilling!"

Then the judges examined the work. And they found that John Henry had sunk a fourteen-foot hole while the steam drill had gone only nine feet down. Wildly the steel drivers shouted, "Hooray! John Henry's saved our jobs! He's proved that a man's worth more'n any machine!"

But the giant Negro hardly heard their shouting. He had stood more than any man could stand. Staggering from the dark tunnel into the sunlight, he fell with his hammer in his hand. Men lifted him and carried him up to a hilltop. They laid him on the grass and he looked at the sky above.

"Wrap my hammer in gold," he said, "and give it to the girl I love! And if I die a steel-drivin' man, go bury me under the sand, a pick and shovel at my head and feet and a nine pound hammer in my hand!"

Then they carried him home to Polly Ann and the children. And they waited before his door till Polly Ann came out to them, weeping.

"John Henry!" she said. "John Henry's dead!"

Then the steel-drivin' men wept, too. Wrapping his hammer in gold, they gave it to Polly Ann. And they crowded to his funeral. Then they put his body on a train and took it to Washington where they buried him close to the President's home at the White House. And they did as he had requested. They placed a pick and shovel at his head and feet and a nine pound hammer in his hand. And they cut these words on his gravestone—

HERE LIES OUR STEEL-DRIVIN' MAN!

HERE LIES OUR STEEL DRIVIN' MAN

143

Why the Sea Is Salt*
A Norse Folk Tale
Gudrun Thorne-Thomsen

ONCE on a time, but it was a long, long time ago, there were two brothers, one rich and one poor. Now, one Christmas eve, the poor one had not so much as a crumb in the house, either of meat or bread, so he went to his brother to ask him for something with which to keep Christmas. It was not the first time his brother had been forced to help him; and, as he was always stingy, he was not very glad to see him this time, but he said, "I'll give you a whole piece of bacon, two loaves of bread, and candles into the bargain, if you'll never bother me again, but mind you don't set foot in my house from this day on."

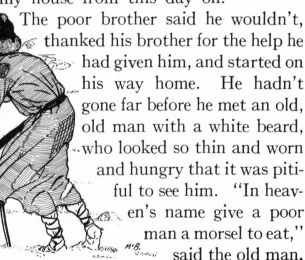

The poor brother said he wouldn't, thanked his brother for the help he had given him, and started on his way home. He hadn't gone far before he met an old, old man with a white beard, who looked so thin and worn and hungry that it was pitiful to see him. "In heaven's name give a poor man a morsel to eat," said the old man.

*From *East o' the Sun and West o' the Moon.* Used by special arrangement with the author and the publisher, Row, Peterson & Co.

"Now, indeed, I have been begging myself," said the poor brother, "but I'm not so poor that I can't give you something on the blessed Christmas eve." And with that he handed the old man a candle and a loaf of bread and he was just going to cut off a slice of bacon, when the old man stopped him. "That is enough and to spare," said he. "And now, I'll tell you something. Not far from here is the entrance to the home of the underground folks. They have a mill there which can grind out anything they wish for except bacon; now mind you go there. When you get inside they will all want to buy your bacon, but don't sell it unless you get in return the mill which stands behind the door. When you come out I'll teach you how to handle the mill."

So the man with the bacon thanked the other for his good advice and followed the directions which the old man had given him, and very soon he stood outside the hillfolks' home. When he got in, everything went just as the old man said. All the hillfolk, great and small, came swarming up to him like ants around an ant hill and each tried to outbid the other for the bacon.

144a

"Well!" said the man, "by rights, my old dame and I ought to have this bacon for our Christmas dinner; but, since you have all set your hearts on it, I suppose I must give it up to you. Now, if I sell it at all, I'll have for it that mill behind the door yonder."

The hillfolk wouldn't hear of such a bargain and higgled and haggled with the man, but he stuck to what he said, and at last they gave up the mill for the bacon.

When the man got out of the cave and into the woods again, he met the same old beggar and asked him how to handle the mill. After he had learned how to use it, he thanked the old man and went off home as fast as he could; still the clock had struck twelve on Christmas eve before he reached his own door.

"Wherever in the world have you been?" asked his old dame. "Here have I sat hour after hour, waiting and watching, without so much as two sticks to lay under the Christmas porridge."

So he put the mill on the table, and bade it first of all to grind out lights, then a tablecloth, then meat, then ale, and so on till they had everything that was nice for Christmas fare. He had only to speak the word and the mill ground out whatever he wanted. On the third day of Christmas he asked his friends and kin to his house and gave them a great feast. Now, when his rich brother saw all that was on the table and all that was in the cupboards, he grew quite wild with anger, for he could not bear that his brother should have anything.

144b

"'Twas only on Christmas eve," he said to the rest, "he was so poorly off that he came and begged for a morsel of food, and now he gives a feast as if he were a count or a king." Then he turned to his brother and said, "But where in the world did you get all this wealth?"

"From behind the door," answered the owner of the mill, for he did not care to tell his brother much about it. But later in the evening, when he had gotten a little too merry, he could keep his secret no longer and he brought out the mill and said:

"There you see what has gotten me all this wealth." And so he made the mill grind all kinds of things.

When his brother saw it, he set his heart on having the mill; and, after some talk, it was agreed that the rich brother was to get it at hay-harvest time, when he was to pay three hundred dollars for it. Now, you may fancy the mill did not grow rusty for want of work; for while he had it, the poor brother made it grind meat and drink that would last for years. When hay-harvest came, the rich brother got it, but he was in such a hurry to make it grind that he forgot to learn how to handle it.

One day, when dinner time drew near, the rich brother put the mill on the kitchen table and said, "Grind herrings and broth, and grind them good and fast."

And the mill began to grind herrings and broth, first of all the dishes full, then all the tubs full, and so on till the kitchen floor was quite covered. The man twisted and twirled at the mill to get it to stop; but, for all his fiddling and fumbling, the mill went on grinding. The broth rose so high that the man was nearly drowned. So he threw open the kitchen door and ran into the parlor, but before long the mill had ground the parlor full and at the risk of his life the man got hold of the latch of the housedoor through the stream of broth. When he got the door open he ran down the road with the stream of herrings and broth roaring at his heels like a waterfall.

The harvesters, who had worked hard in the fields tossing hay, sauntered home for dinner. Halfway down the hill what should they meet but herrings and broth all running and dashing and splashing together in a stream and the master, himself, running before them for his life. As he passed them he called out: "Eat, drink! Eat, drink! but take care you're not drowned in the broth."

Away he ran as fast as his legs would carry him to his brother's house and begged him in heaven's name to take back the mill at once and he said, "If it grinds only one hour more the whole parish will be swallowed up by herrings and broth."

So the poor brother took back the mill and it stopped grinding herrings and broth. He set up a farmhouse far finer than his brother's. The house was very large and located by the sea. It was covered with plates of gold which were ground by the mill. As the farm lay by the seaside, the golden house could be seen glistening from far out at sea. All who sailed by put ashore to see the rich man in the golden house and his wonderful mill.

One day a skipper came to see the mill and he asked if it could grind salt. "Grind salt!" said the owner, "I should think it can! It can grind anything." The skipper knew he could sell salt for great riches and he asked to keep the mill. The man let him have it, but the skipper was in such a hurry that he had no time to ask how to handle the mill. He got on board his ship as fast as he could and set sail. He brought the mill on deck and said, "Grind salt, and grind both good and fast." And the mill began to grind salt so that it poured out like water; and when the skipper had got the ship full he could not stop the mill. The mill kept on grinding, the heap of salt grew higher, and at last down sank the ship. There lies the mill at the bottom of the sea and grinds away to this day, and that is why the sea is salt.

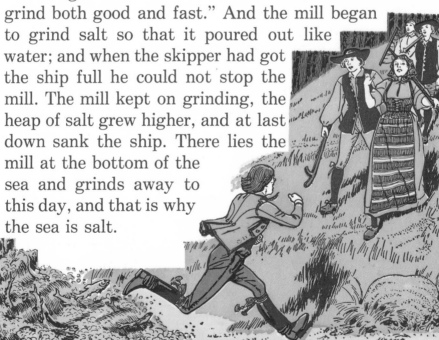

Heidi in the Alpine Pasture

From HEIDI by Johanna Spyri*

HEIDI was awakened by a loud whistle. She had just come to live with her grandfather high up in the Alps, the snow-capped mountains of Switzerland. Jumping out of her little hay bed, she dressed, climbed down the ladder from the loft where she slept and ran out of doors. There stood the boy Peter with the goats he took every day to feed on pastures still higher up. Grandfather was bringing his two goats from the shed to join Peter's flock and he said, "Heidi, would you like to go with Peter and the goats?"

Heidi jumped for joy. Then her grandfather bade Peter to open the bag in which he carried his dinner. Scanty enough it was, for Peter was poor and only herded other people's goats.

Putting into the bag slices of bread and cheese twice as big as Peter's, Grandfather said, "This is for Heidi's dinner. Now the mug goes in also. Milk it full twice for Heidi. And mind this—you're to take care of her. You're to see that she doesn't fall off over the edge of a cliff."

Happily, Heidi and Peter started off up the mountain. The sun shone brightly on the green slopes and Heidi ran hither and yon, shouting with delight, as she saw whole patches of red, blue, and yellow flowers. First one way, then the other she ran, as she caught sight of some new spot of bright color. And she picked handfuls of

*Johanna Spyri was a great Swiss writer, who knew what life was like high up in the mountains of Switzerland.

flowers, putting them into her apron so she could take them home. Peter had to be on the alert every instant, for the goats were as lively as Heidi. They, too, ran in all directions, and Peter had to follow them, whistling, calling and swinging his stick to get all the runaways together again.

Finally he called out, "Heidi! Heidi! Where are you?"

"Here!" a voice called from somewhere. Peter could see no one, for Heidi was sitting behind a flowery hill.

"Come back here!" Peter shouted. But Heidi was too interested in the flowers to obey him. So he added, "Come, I say! We still have a long way to go. But if you climb up to the highest pasture maybe you'll see a great bird—the old eagle, who sits there and screams."

That did it. Heidi wanted to see the old eagle. Jumping up, she ran to Peter with her apron full of flowers.

After that, she kept along with Peter. The goats also went in better order, for they were beginning to smell the plants they loved which grew on the higher slopes.

Up and up they climbed until they reached a patch of green grass at the foot of great gray rocks from which scrubby little bushes cropped out. This was where Peter usually halted his flock to pasture for the day. Now he placed his bag in a little hollow where it could not be blown away, for he knew what the wind was like up there at such a height. Untying her apron, Heidi wrapped it around her flowers and laid it by Peter's bag. Then Peter lay down on the ground to rest while Heidi sat beside him and looked about on every side.

This beautiful picture of Heidi and Peter was painted by the great American illustrator, N. C. Wyeth, and selected from the *Anthology of Children's Literature*, published by Houghton Mifflin Company. The original painting may be seen at the Free Library of Philadelphia. Used by courtesy of LIFE Magazine.

Far below her lay the green valley, its patchwork of fields bathed in the sunlight. Before her, a broad snowfield on a mountain top shone white against the blue sky. And all around her rose other towering, jagged peaks. Peter had fallen asleep and the goats were climbing about among the rocks above her, looking for their favorite tidbits.

Never had Heidi felt so happy. A long time she sat there while the mountains seemed to take on faces and look down on her like old friends. Then suddenly she heard a piercing scream overhead. Lifting her eyes, she saw a bird, larger than any bird she had ever seen before. With its great, spreading wings it was wheeling round and round in circles, croaking and screaming.

"Peter, wake up!" she cried. "The great bird—the eagle! Look! Look! It's here!"

Rubbing his eyes, Peter sat up. Then they both watched the bird, which rose higher and higher in the sky until it disappeared behind a mountain top.

"Where has it gone?" Heidi asked.

"Home to its nest," Peter answered.

"Oh, how nice to live up so high!" Heidi squealed. "Let's climb up and see where its nest is!"

"Oh, you!" Peter snorted in disgust at her ignorance. "Don't you know that even the goats can't climb as high as that? And didn't your grandfather say you were not to fall off over the edge of a cliff?"

Then he sprang up and began whistling and calling to the goats. One by one, they came leaping down the rocks until they were all gathered on the patch of grass. Some started nibbling on the grass, some just ran about and some butted playfully at each other with their horns.

Running in among them, Heidi went hopping and jumping from one to another. Each goat was so different from any other and Heidi wanted to know them all.

Some let her stroke and pet them, some dashed skittishly from her. Then there was one big fellow with huge horns who seemed to think he was lord of the flock and was always butting the others. But the one that interested Heidi most was a little young goat who bleated so pitifully that Heidi ran up and put her arms around its neck trying to comfort it.

Meantime, Peter took the bag out of the hollow and placed the slices of bread and cheese on the ground in the shape of a square, the larger two on Heidi's side and the smaller on his own, for he knew exactly which were hers and which were his. Then he took the mug and milked it full from Little Swan, Heidi's grandfather's pretty white goat. And when all was ready, he cried:

"Heidi, stop hopping and jumping! Come! It's dinner time."

So Heidi came and sat down.

Slowly Heidi drank her milk while Peter ate. But as soon as her mug was empty he rose and filled it for her again. Then she broke off some of her bread and held out the rest to Peter. It was a big piece, twice as large as his, which he had already eaten. And in her other hand she held out her whole big lump of cheese.

"You may have this. I've had enough," she said.

Peter stared at her, speechless, his eyes big with astonishment. Never in his life had he been able to say that he had had enough to eat and had food left to give away. But when he saw that Heidi really meant what she said, he nodded his thanks, took the bread and cheese and enjoyed the heartiest meal he had eaten since he started to work as a goatherd. While they ate, Heidi said, "Peter, tell me the names of all the goats."

So Peter began to name them one after another, pointing out each with his finger. Soon Heidi, too, could name them all. There was the Great Turk—he was the one with the huge horns who tried to lord it over the others by butting at them fiercely and not in play. Most of the other goats ran away when they saw the Great Turk coming. Only the slender, nimble little Greenfinch had the courage to face him. She rushed at him three or four times in succession so swiftly and boldly that the Great Turk stood still, astounded, and did not venture to attack her again. Then there was little white Snowflake, the one who bleated in such a pitiful, beseeching way. Now it sounded to Heidi as though Snowflake was in some trouble and begging for help.

Jumping up, Heidi ran to the little goat, put her arms around its neck again and asked, "What's the matter, little Snowflake? Why do you cry like that?"

"She cries because the old goat is not with her," Peter called from where he was sitting. "The old goat was sold the day before yesterday. She'll never come up the mountain with us again."

"The old goat—who is the old goat?" Heidi called back.

"Why, her mother, of course," Peter answered shortly.

"But if her mother can't come, why doesn't her grandmother come?" Heidi asked.

"Has no grandmother!"

"Then why doesn't her grandfather come?"

"Has no grandfather!"

"Oh, you poor little Snowflake!" Heidi clasped the goat gently to her. "Don't cry like that. I'll come up here with you every day, so you won't be alone any more."

Then Snowflake rubbed her head contentedly against Heidi's shoulder, and stopped her pitiful bleating.

When Peter had finished eating, he came up and joined Heidi. By this time the goats had begun to climb the rocks toward the bushes again, each in its own manner, some springing swiftly from rock to rock, others going slowly, searching for some tasty morsel.

"Peter," Heidi said, "the prettiest of all the goats are Grandfather's Little Swan and Little Bear."

"That's because your grandfather brushes them down and washes them and gives them salt and keeps them in a good shed," Peter answered.

But he had scarcely spoken when he let out a startled cry and dashed off in a hurry. Heidi ran after him, wondering where he was going and why he was going so fast. Through the flock of goats he raced—on, on and up— up toward a spot where the rock of the mountain side fell down, sheer and steep, to a very great depth below. It was just such a cliff as Grandfather had told Peter to look out for lest Heidi should fall over it. Yet now she was racing straight toward it, following swiftly at Peter's heels.

That nimble, bold, inquisitive, ever adventurous little goat, Greenfinch! She who wasn't afraid even of the Great Turk! Peter had spied her leaping off toward the danger spot on a journey of exploration. And he reached her just in time. There she stood on the very edge of the cliff, ready to plunge down over it to see what lay in the world beyond. Peter put out his hand to seize her, but as he did so, he tripped and fell flat to the ground, catching hold of her only by one of her hind legs.

Furious at being prevented from continuing her trip of discovery, Greenfinch struggled to get free, still stubbornly bent on leaping forward. Peter could not get up without letting go of her leg. So he lay there, holding so fast to her leg that he was afraid he might pull it off.

"Heidi! Heidi! Help!" he called.

Quickly Heidi picked some sweet-smelling leaves of the kind that goats loved best. Then she came running. Standing close to the edge of the cliff, she held the leaves out temptingly under Greenfinch's nose.

"Come, little goat! Be good!" she cried. "You mustn't fall over the cliff! You might break your legs."

But it wasn't Heidi's words, it was the leaves that stopped Greenfinch from straining forward. One smell of those leaves and Greenfinch forgot all about her intended journey of exploration. Turning around, she started nibbling at the leaves and as Heidi drew them back a little, then a little more, Greenfinch followed, hobbling on three legs but still nibbling, until she was safe and out of danger at last.

Then Peter let go of her leg, sprang to his feet and seized the string that hung from her collar, while Heidi took the collar from the other side. Thus they led the adventurous Greenfinch to rejoin the rest of the flock which was now feeding peacefully in the green pasture.

The day seemed to pass in no time. All too soon the sun began to sink behind the mountains. Heidi sat down on the ground. Quietly, she watched while a golden light spread over all the earth, turning the grass and the flowers to gold and making the rocks above her glow and shine and flash. Then suddenly she sprang up.

"Peter, look!" she cried. "Everything's on fire! Everything's burning—the great snow mountain, the rocks and the sky! Look, look! That highest peak—it's all aflame! And the beautiful white snow—it's fiery red!"

"It's always like that at this time of day," Peter answered calmly. "But it isn't fire."

"What is it, then?" Heidi ran about in every direction, for she could not see enough standing still, it was so beautiful everywhere. "Peter, what is it?"

"It's something that just happens," Peter answered, shrugging his shoulders. But Heidi screamed in another burst of excitement:

"Look! Now everything's turned the color of roses. Look at the lovely rosy snow! And those high pointed rocks—they're covered with roses!"

Then in another moment she cried out in distress:

"It's going! O Peter, it's going! Everything's growing gray! The color's going! It's going! O Peter, it's gone, it's all gone!" And she threw herself down on the ground, looking as unhappy as if the end of the world had come.

"It will be the same tomorrow," Peter said. "Come now. We must go home." But Heidi demanded:

"Will it surely be like that tomorrow?"

155

"It's like that most days," Peter replied. Then he whistled to his flock to gather them together and he and Heidi and the goats all started out for home.

Heidi's mind was so full of all she had seen and done that day that she hardly spoke until she saw her grandfather waiting for her on the bench before his cottage. Then she left Peter and darted toward her grandfather, while Little Swan and Little Bear rushed on ahead of her, for they knew their own master and their own shed.

But Peter called out, "Good night, Heidi! Come with me again tomorrow!"

So Heidi ran back to him, clasped his hand and promised to go with him every day. Then she said good night to each of his flock and flung her arms around Snowflake's neck, saying, "Don't be sad, little Snowflake. You'll never be alone again. I'll be with you every day!"

When Peter and the goats had gone, Heidi skipped back to her grandfather, crying, "It was so beautiful! The fire and the roses on the rocks! Grandfather, what makes the mountains look like that when the sun sets?"

"That's how the sun says good night to the mountains," Grandfather explained. "He throws his most beautiful colors across them, so they won't forget he's coming again in the morning." This pleased Heidi and she could scarcely wait until the next day to go out and see the same sights over again.

That night, as she slept in her little hay bed in the loft, she dreamed of shining mountains covered with roses among which Snowflake jumped gaily about.

Boots and His Brothers

SIR GEORGE WEBBE DASENT*

Once upon a time there was a man who had three sons, Peter, Paul, and Jack. Jack was Boots, of course, because he was the youngest. The man had only these three sons, for he hadn't one penny to rub against another; and so he told his sons they must try to earn their bread. A short way from the man's cottage was the king's palace, and against the king's windows a great oak had sprung up so big it took away all the light. The king said he would give many dollars to a man who could fell the oak. But as soon as one chip of the oak's trunk flew off, two grew in its stead. A well, too, the king would have dug. He said he would give both money and goods to anyone who could dig him such a well that would hold water for a whole year. But no one could do it, for the king's palace lay high up on a hill, and they hadn't dug a few inches before they came upon rock.

But the king had set his heart on having these two things done. He an-

*Dasent is one of the famous collectors of Norse folk tales. He did for the Norse people what the Grimms did for the Germans and Joseph Jacobs for the English. From *Popular Tales from the Norse*, published by G. P. Putnam's Sons.

nounced that the man who could fell the oak and dig a well
that would hold water for a whole year, should have the
Princess and half the kingdom. Well, you may easily know
there was many a man who came to try his luck, but for all
their hacking and hewing and all their digging and delving,
it was no good. The oak got bigger and stouter at every
stroke, and the rock didn't get softer either. So, one day,
those three brothers thought they'd set off and try. Their
father hadn't a word against it, so Peter, Paul, and Jack
went off from their home.

Well, they hadn't gone far before they came to a fir wood
and up along one side of it rose a steep hillside; and, as
they went, they heard something hewing and hacking up
on the hill among the trees. "I wonder what it is that is
hewing away up yonder," said Jack.

"You're always so clever with your wonderings," said
Peter and Paul. "What wonder is it that a woodcutter
should stand and hack up there on a hillside?"

"I'd like to see what it is," said Jack, and up he went.

"If you're such a child, 'twill do you good to go and take
a lesson," bawled out his brothers. But Jack didn't care
what they said; he climbed the steep hillside toward the
source of the noise; and, when he reached the place he saw
an axe hacking, all of itself, at the trunk of a fir. "Good-
day!" said Jack. "So you hack away by yourself?"

"Yes. Here I've stood and hewed and hacked a long,
long time, waiting for you," said the Axe.

"Well, here I am at last," said Jack and pulled the axe
head off its shaft and stuffed both into his wallet.

So when he got down again to his brothers, they began to jeer at him. "And now, what funny thing was it you saw up yonder on the hillside?" they said.

"Oh, it was only an axe we heard," said Jack.

So, when they had gone a bit farther, they came under a steep rock and up there they heard something digging and shoveling. "I wonder now," said Jack, "what it is digging and shoveling up yonder at the top of the rock."

"Ah, you're always so clever with your wonderings," said Peter and Paul again, "as if you'd never heard a woodpecker hacking and pecking at a hollow tree.

"Well," said Jack, "I think it would be a piece of fun just to see what it really is." So off he set to climb the rock; and, when he got near the top, what do you think he saw? Why a spade that stood there digging and delving.

"Good-day!" said Jack. "So you stand here all alone, and dig and delve!"

"Yes," said the Spade, "and that's what I've done this many a long day, waiting for you."

"Well, here I am," said Jack again, as he took the spade and knocked it off its handle, put it into his wallet, and then went down again to his brothers.

"Well, what was it, so rare and strange," said Peter and Paul, "that you saw up there at the top of the rock?"

"Oh," said Jack, "nothing more than a spade."

So they went on again a good bit, till they came to a brook. "I wonder now," said Jack, "where all this water comes from."

"Where the brook comes from, indeed!" said Peter and Paul in one breath.

"I've a great fancy to see where this brook comes from," said Jack. So up he went; and as he went, the brook got smaller and smaller. At last, farther on he saw a great walnut out of which the water trickled. "Good-day!" said Jack again. "So you lie here, and trickle and run down all alone?"

"Yes, I do," said the Walnut, "and I've trickled and run many a long day, waiting for you."

"Well, here I am," said Jack and he plugged up the hole with a lump of moss so the water wouldn't run out. Then he put the walnut into his wallet and joined his brothers.

"Well," said Peter and Paul, "have you found out where the water comes from?"

"Oh, it was only a hole it ran out of," said Jack; and so the others laughed and made fun of him again.

When they had gone farther, they came to the king's

160

palace. The two brothers were quite sure they could fell the oak; and Peter, as the eldest, was to try first; but it went with him as with all the rest who had hewn at the oak; for every chip he cut out, two grew in its place. Now Paul was to try, but he failed too. Now Jack was to try.

The King and his brothers just laughed, but Jack took his axe out of his wallet and fitted it to its shaft. "Hew away!" said he to his axe; and away it hewed, making the chips fly so fast that it wasn't long before the oak crashed to the ground. Then Jack pulled out his spade, fitted it to its handle, and said, "Dig away!" The spade began to dig and earth and rock flew out in heaps.

And, when the well was as big and as deep as the king wanted, Jack pulled out the walnut, removed the plug of moss, and laid it in one corner of the well.

"Trickle and run!" said Jack; and so the nut trickled and ran, till the water gushed out of the hole in a stream and in a short time the well was brimful.

Since Jack had felled the oak which shaded the King's palace and dug a well in the palace yard, he got the Princess and half the kingdom, as the King had promised. Everyone said, "Well, after all, Jack wasn't so much out of his mind when he took to wondering."

The Nuremberg Stove*
LOUISE DE LA RAMÉE

AUGUST lived in a little town called Hall in Austria. His mother was dead, his father was poor, and there were many mouths at home to feed. This night was terribly cold, but he kept up his courage by saying: "I shall soon be at home with dear Hirschvogel." The snow outlined with white every gable and cornice of the beautiful, old, wooden houses; the moonlight shone on the gilded signs that hung before the doors. Here and there a ruddy firelight lit up a homely interior, with the noisy band of children clustering around the housemother.

At August's knock, the oak door of his father's house flew open. It was a large, barren room into which he rushed; but, at the top of the chamber, sending out warmth and color, was a tower of porcelain, surmounted with armed figures and shields and a great golden crown on the summit of all. It was a stove of 1532, the handwork of the great potter, Augustin Hirschvogel.

*Nuremberg was once an art center for Germany. Longfellow calls it "quaint old town of art and song," and Wagner's opera, *Die Meistersinger von Nürnberg*, portrays its famous mastersingers of the 16th Century.

The stove, no doubt, had stood in palaces and been made for princes; had warmed the crimson stockings of cardinals and the gold-broidered shoes of archduchesses. It was a right royal thing. Yet, perhaps, it had never been more useful than it was now in this poor, desolate room, sending down heat and comfort to the troop of children tumbled together on a wolfskin at its feet.

"Oh, dear Hirschvogel, I am so cold!" said August, kissing its gilded lion's claws. "Is father not in, Dorothea?"

"No, dear. He is late."

Dorothea was seventeen, the eldest of the Strehla family; there were ten of them in all. Next to her, came Jan and Karl and Otho, big lads, gaining a little for their own living. And then came August, who went up in the summer to the high Alps with the farmers' cattle, but in winter could do nothing. And then all the little ones, who could only open their mouths to be fed like young birds—Albrecht and Hilda, and Waldo and Christof, and last of all little three-year-old Ermengilda, with eyes like forget-me-nots.

The father was a good man, but weak and weary with so many to find food for and so little to do it with. He worked at the salt furnaces; and, by that, gained a few florins. Very poor they were, and Dorothea's heart ached with shame, for she knew that their father's debts were many for flour and meat and clothing. Of fuel to feed the big stove, they had always enough without cost, for their mother's father was alive and sold wood and fir cones and coke, and never grudged them to his grandchildren.

"Father says we are never to wait for him. We will have supper, now you have come home, dear," said Dorothea.

Supper was a huge bowl of soup, with big slices of brown bread swimming in it, and some onions bobbing up and down. The bowl was soon emptied by ten wooden spoons; and then the three eldest boys slipped off to bed, being tired with their rough bodily labor in the snow all day. Dorothea drew her spinning wheel by the stove and set it whirring, and the little ones got August down upon the old worn wolfskin and clamored to him for a picture or a story. For August was the artist of the family.

He had a piece of planed wood, that his father had given him, and some sticks of charcoal and he would draw a hundred things he had seen in the day—faces and dogs' heads, and men in sledges. It was all very rough, for there was no one to teach him anything, but it kept the whole troop of children shrieking with laughter or watching breathlessly with wide-open, wondering eyes.

They were all so happy; what did they care for the snow outside? Their little bodies were warm, and their hearts merry; and August cried, as he looked at the stove shedding its heat on them all: "Oh, dear Hirschvogel, you are almost as great and good as the sun! No, you are greater and better, because he goes away all these dark, cold hours; but you—just a bit of wood to feed you—and you make a summer for us all the winter through!"

The grand old stove seemed to smile through all its iridescent surface at the praises of the child. The grandfather Strehla, who had been a master mason, had dug it up out of some ruins where he was building, and only thought it worth finding because it was such a good one to burn. Ever since then the stove had stood in the big, empty room—having seen nothing prettier in all its many years than the children tumbled now in a cluster, like gathered flowers, at its feet.

To the children, the stove was a household god. In summer, they dressed it up with green boughs and the numberless beautiful wild flowers of the Tyrol. In winter, all their joys centered in it; and, scampering home from school over the ice and snow, they were happy knowing that they would soon be cracking nuts or roasting chest-

nuts in the broad, ardent glow of its noble tower with all
its spires and pinnacles. All the children loved the stove;
but, with August, the love of it was a passion, and in his
secret heart he used to say to himself, "When I am a man,
I will make just such things!" For August was a dreamer
of dreams, and when high up on the Alps with the stillness
and the sky around him, he was quite certain that he would
live for greater things than driving the herds up when the
springtide came among the blue sea of gentians.

In the midst of the chatter and laughter, a blast of
frozen air struck like ice through the room. It was the
father who had come home. The younger children ran to
meet him, but Karl Strehla responded wearily to the

young ones' welcome. "Take the children to bed," he said, and Dorothea obeyed. August stayed behind, curled before the stove. When Dorothea came down again, suddenly Karl Strehla struck his hand on the table.

"I have sold Hirschvogel," he said; and his voice was husky in his throat. "I have sold Hirschvogel to a traveling trader for two-hundred florins. What would you? I owe double that. He will take it to Munich tomorrow."

Dorothea gave a low cry, "Oh, Father!—the children— in midwinter!" She turned white as the snow without.

August stood staring with dazed eyes. He gave a shriek and threw himself down at his father's feet.

"Oh, Father!" he cried, his hands closing on Strehla's knees. "You cannot mean what you say! Send *it* away— our life, our sun, our joy, our comfort? You could not do such a thing! It is a living thing, and it loves us and we love it with all our hearts! Oh, listen! I will go and try and get work tomorrow! I will ask them to let me cut ice or make the paths through the snow. Oh, Father, do hear me, for pity's sake!"

Strehla was moved by the boy's anguish. Every word of the child stung him with a sense of shame. He despised himself for the barter of the heirloom of his race. "You are a little fool," he said, harshly, as they had never heard him speak. "Get up and go to bed. The stove is sold and goes to Munich tomorrow."

Then Strehla took the oil-lamp and stumbled off to bed.

August threw himself on the stove, covering it with kisses, and sobbing as though his heart would burst.

"Come to bed, dear. Oh, don't lie and look like that!" sighed his sister.

"I shall stay here. They might take it in the night!"

"But it is cold! The fire is out."

"It will never be warm any more, nor shall we."

All his childhood had gone out of him, all his gleeful, careless, sunny temper. To him it was as if the end of the world had come. His sister lingered by him while striving to persuade him to go to his place in the little crowded bedchamber with Albrecht and Waldo and Christof. But it was in vain. "I shall stay here," was all he answered her. And he stayed—all the night long. The lamps went out; the rats came and ran across the floor; the cold intensified and the air of the room grew like ice. Whilst yet it was dark, his three elder brothers let themselves out—each going to his work. His sister came down with a light in her hand. August shuddered all over. "It is the morning!" he said.

Loud blows with the heavy, iron knocker drowned his words. A strange voice called aloud: "Let me in! Quick! I am come to take the great stove."

August sprang erect, his fists doubled, his eyes blazing. "You shall never touch it!" he screamed.

"Who shall prevent us?" laughed a big man, amused at the fierce little figure fronting him.

"I!" said August. "You shall never have it!"

"Strehla," said the big man, as August's father entered the room, "you have got a little mad dog here, muzzle him."

August fought like a little demon, and hit out right and left. But he was soon mastered by four grown men, and his father flung him with no light hand out the door.

When Dorothea stole out to look for August, he was nowhere in sight. She went back to little Gilda and sobbed, whilst the others stood looking on, dimly understanding that with Hirschvogel was going all the warmth of their bodies and the light of their hearth.

August stood still for a time leaning against the back wall of the house. Then his heart fluttered with a new idea. Why not go with the stove? He ran out of the court-

yard and across to the huge Gothic porch of the church. From there he could watch unseen his father's door.

Presently his heart gave a great leap, for he saw the straw-enwrapped stove brought out and laid with infinite care on the bullock dray. The sleigh-wagon slowly crept over the snow of the place. Then he crept, unseen by any of his brothers or sisters, out of the porch and followed in the wake of the dray. A desperate resolve made itself up in August's mind. Where Hirschvogel went, he would go. How he managed it he never knew; but certain it is that, when the goods-train moved out of Hall, August was hidden behind the stove in one of the cars.

It was very dark in the car, but August was not frightened, he was close to Hirschvogel and presently he meant to be closer; for he meant to do nothing less than get inside Hirschvogel itself. Having by great luck two silver groschen in his pocket, which he had earned the day before by chopping wood, he had bought some bread and sausage at the station. This he ate in the darkness.

When he had eaten, he set to work like a little mouse to make a hole in the straw and hay which enveloped the stove. He gnawed and nibbled and pulled, making his hole where he guessed that the opening of the stove was, the opening through which he had so often thrust the big, oak logs to feed it. At last he found the door of the stove, which he knew was quite large enough for a child of his age to slip through. Slip through he did, as he had often done at home for fun, and curled himself up there to see if he could remain during many hours.

He found that he could, air came in through the brass fretwork of the stove. He leaned out, drew the hay and straw together, and re-arranged the ropes so that no one could ever have dreamed a little mouse had been at them. Then he curled himself up again and went fast asleep. The train lumbered on and, when he awoke, it was quite

dark. For awhile he was sorely frightened and sobbed in a heartbroken fashion, thinking of them all at home.

It took all the short winter's day and the long winter's night and half of another day to go over ground that the mailtrains cover in a forenoon. The train passed pretty Rosenheim, and here the Nuremberg stove was lifted out heedfully and set under a covered way. The boy was tossed to and fro as the men lifted the huge thing, and the walls of his beloved fire king were not cushions of down.

He had still some of his loaf and a little of his sausage. What he did begin to suffer was thirst. But, fortunately for him, the stove, having been marked "fragile and valuable," was not treated like a mere bale of goods; and the Rosenheim stationmaster resolved to send it on by a passenger train that would leave there at daybreak.

Munich was reached; and August, shaking like a little aspen leaf, felt himself once more carried out on the shoulders of men, rolled along on a truck, and finally set down, where he knew not, only he knew he was thirsty—so thirsty! He thought he had been moved on this truck many miles; but, in truth, the stove had been only taken from the railway station to a shop in the Marienplatz. On its gilded feet it now stood in the small, dark curiosity-shop of one Hans Rhilfer.

"I shall not unpack it till Anton comes," he heard a man's voice say; and then he heard a key grate in a lock. He concluded he was alone, and ventured to peep through the straw and hay. What he saw was a small, square room filled with pictures, carvings, old steel armor, shields, daggers, Chinese idols, and all the rubbish of a *bric-a-brac* dealer's. It seemed a wonderful place; but, oh! was there one drop of water in it all? There was not a drop of water, but beyond the window was a wide stone ledge covered with snow. August darted out of his hiding-place, ran and opened the window, crammed the snow into his mouth, and then flew back into the stove.

Presently the key turned in the lock, he heard heavy footsteps and the voice of the man who had said to his father, "You have a little mad dog, muzzle him!" The voice said, "You have called me a fool many times. Now you shall see what I have got for two-hundred dirty florins!"

Then the two men approached more closely, and the heart of the child went pit-a-pat. They began to strip the stove of its wrappings.

"A right royal thing! Sublime! Magnificent!" they said.

August fancied at times they quarreled, for they swore lustily. He made out that they were going to show Hirschvogel to some great person.

Presently the door opened again sharply. He could hear the two dealers' voices murmuring unctuous words. The voice of another person, more clear and refined than theirs, answered them curtly. The child could distinguish little that he said, except the name of the king and the word "gulden" again and again. After awhile, he went away. Then the dealers also withdrew, double-locking the door.

After a time, August dropped asleep. Midnight was

chiming when he awoke and, all being still, ventured to
put his head out the door of the stove to see why such a
strange, bright light was round him. What he saw was
nothing less than all the *bric-a-brac* in motion.

A tall, Dutch clock was going through a gavotte with
a spindle-legged chair; an old violin of Cremona was playing itself; a Japanese bronze was riding along on a griffin.
Little Dresden cups and saucers were skipping and waltz-
ing; the teapots with their broad, round faces were spinning
their own lids like teetotums; and a little Saxe poodle
with a red ribbon at its throat, was running from one to
another. A lovely, little lady all in pink and gold and
white, with powdered hair and high-heeled shoes all made of
the finest Meissen china, tripped up to August and smiled
and led him out to a minuet. "I am the Princess of Saxe-
Royale," she said with a smile.

Then he ventured to say to her, "Madame, my Princess, could you tell me kindly why some of the figures dance and speak and some lie up in a corner like lumber?"

"My dear child," said the powdered lady, "those silent, dull things are *imitation*, lies, falsehoods, fabrications! They only *pretend* to be what we *are*?"

Then from where the great stove stood, there came a solemn voice. All eyes turned upon Hirschvogel, and the heart of its little human comrade gave a great jump of joy.

"My friends," said that clear voice, "we were made in days when men were true creators, and so we, the work of their hands, are true, too. Our makers wrought at us with zeal, with integrity, with faith—not to win fortunes, but to do nobly an honest thing and create for the honor of the Arts and God. I see amidst you a little human

thing who loves me. Now I want him forever to remember that we are what we are, because those who were of single mind so created us, scorning sham and haste and counterfeit. Where I go now I know not; but, since I go from that humble house where they loved me, I shall be sad and alone."

Then the voice sank away in silence, and a strange golden light that had shone on the great stove faded away. The clocks of the city struck six of the morning. August awoke with a start and found himself lying on the bare bricks of the floor, and all the *bric-a-brac* was lying quite still all around.

He rose slowly to his feet. Tramp, tramp, came a heavy step up the stair. He had but a moment in which to scramble back into the great stove, when the door opened and the two dealers entered, bringing candles with them to see their way. The dealers undid the shutters and then began to wrap up the stove once more in all its straw and hay. Presently they called up their porters, and the stove, heedfully swathed and tended as though it were some prince going on a journey, was borne on the shoulders of six stout Bavarians down the stairs and out the door. Even behind all those wrappings August felt the icy bite of the intense cold at dawn of a winter's day in Munich.

The stout carriers tramped right across Munich to the railway station. Whether for a long or a short journey, whether for weal or woe, the stove with August still within it, was once more hoisted up into a great van; but this time it was not all alone, and the two dealers as well as the six porters were all with it.

Though the men grumbled about the state of the roads and the season, they were hilarious and well-content, for they laughed often; and August, like the shrewd little boy he was, thought to himself, with a terrible pang, "They have sold Hirschvogel for some great sum! They have sold him already!"

It is but an hour and a quarter that the train usually takes to pass from Munich to the Lake of Starnberg; but this morning the journey was much slower, because the way was encumbered by snow. When it did reach Possenhofen, the stove was lifted out once more. August could see through the fretwork of the brass door a calm and noble piece of water with low, wooded banks and distant mountains. Before he had time to get more than a glimpse of the green, gliding surface, the stove was again lifted up and placed on a large boat that was in waiting. The boat then moved across the lake to Leoni.

"Now, men, for a stout mile and a half!" said one of the dealers to his porters. Encouraged by large promises, they shouldered sullenly the Nuremberg stove, grumbling again at its preposterous weight, but little dreaming that they carried within it a small, panting, trembling boy. The road seemed terribly long to the poor little man inside the stove as he kept sinking and rising, sinking and rising with each of their steps.

After a very long time August lost the sense of the fresh, icy wind blowing on his face through the brasswork above. Then he heard a great many voices, and, as he felt a warm

air come to him, he concluded that he was in some heated chambers. There was a delicious fragrance in the air—a fragrance as of flowers. "Only how can it be flowers?" thought August. "It is November!" From afar off, as it seemed, there came dreamy, exquisite music. He did not know it, but he was in the royal castle of Berg, and the music he heard was the music of Wagner, who was playing in a distant room.

Presently he heard a low voice say, close behind him, "So! It was well-bought! It is exceedingly beautiful! It is undoubtedly the work of Augustin Hirschvogel."

Then the hand of the speaker turned the round handle of the door, and the fainting soul of the poor little prisoner grew sick with fear. The door was slowly drawn open, someone bent down and looked in, and the same voice called aloud in surprise, "What is this in it? A live child!"

Then August, dominated by one master passion, sprang out of the stove and fell at the feet of the speaker.

"Oh, let me stay! Pray, *mein Herr*, let me stay!" he sobbed. "I have come all the way with Hirschvogel!"

Some gentlemen's hands seized him, not gently by any means, and their lips muttered in his ear. "Little knave, peace! Be quiet! Hold your tongue! It is the King!"

But the voice he had heard said in kind accents, "Poor child! He is very young. Let him go. Let him speak to me."

Richard Wagner (1813-1883), the great German composer, whose music August heard, is the man in the black cap at the right of the picture. King Ludwig II, of Bavaria, friend of all artists, invited Wagner to Munich.

The angry and astonished chamberlains let August slide out of their grasp. The young man said to him, "My child, how come you here, hidden in this stove?"

"Oh, dear King!" said August, "Hirschvogel was ours. We have loved it all our lives, and father sold it. I pray you to let me live with it. I will go out every morning and cut wood for it, if only you will let me stay beside it."

There was that in the child's face which pleased and touched the king. "What is your name?" he asked.

"August Strehla." The boy's lips quivered with a sob.

"Have you traveled in this stove all the way from Tyrol?"

"Yes," said August, "no one thought to look inside till you did." The king laughed; then another view of the matter occurred to him. "Who bought the stove of your father?" he inquired.

"Traders of Munich," said August.

"What sum did they pay, do you know?"

"Two-hundred florins," said August.

The king turned to his gentlemen-in-waiting and desired that the dealers be brought before him. Then he had water and wine brought, and cake also for August, who, though he drank eagerly, could not swallow anything.

"May I stay with Hirschvogel?" he said.

"Wait a little," said the king, and asked abruptly, "what do you wish to be when you are a man?"

"A painter. I wish to be what Hirschvogel was. I mean the master that made *my* Hirschvogel."

"I understand," said the king.

Then the two dealers were brought to their sovereign.

"Did you buy this stove of this boy's father for two-hundred florins?" the king asked, and his voice was no longer soft and kind, but very stern.

"Yes, your Majesty," murmured the trembling traders.

"And how much did the gentleman, who purchased it for me, give to you?"

"Two-thousand ducats!" muttered the dealers.

"You will give at once to this boy's father the two-thousand gold ducats that you received, less the two-hundred Austrian florins that you paid him," said the king. "You are great rogues. Be thankful you are not more greatly punished."

August heard and felt dazzled, yet miserable. Two-thousand ducats for his father! Why, his father would never need to go any more to the salt-baking! And yet, whether for ducats or for florins, Hirschvogel was sold just the same, and would the king let him stay with it?

"Oh, do! please do!" he murmured.

"Will I let you stay with your Hirschvogel?" said the king. "Yes, I will. You shall stay at my court and you shall be taught to be a painter. And if, when you are twenty-one-years old, you have done well and bravely, then I will give you your Nuremberg stove."

Then he smiled and stretched out his hand. The courtiers tried to make August understand that he ought to bow and touch it with his lips, but August was too happy. He threw his arms about the king's knees.

Mowgli's Brothers
FROM THE JUNGLE BOOK BY RUDYARD KIPLING

IT WAS seven o'clock of a very warm evening in the
Seeonee hills when Father Wolf woke up from his
day's rest, scratched himself, yawned, and spread out his
paws one after the other to get rid of the sleepy feeling
in their tips. Mother Wolf lay with her big grey nose

dropped across her four tumbling, squealing cubs, and the moon shone into the mouth of the cave where they all lived. "Augrh!" said Father Wolf. "It is time to hunt again." And he was going to spring down hill when a little shadow with a bushy tail crossed the threshold and whined: "Good luck go with you, O Chief of the Wolves, and good luck and strong white teeth go with your noble children, that they may never forget the hungry in this world."

It was the jackal — Tabaqui, the Dish-licker — and the wolves of India despise Tabaqui because he runs about making mischief, and telling tales, and eating rags and pieces of leather from the village rubbish-heaps. But they are afraid of him too, because Tabaqui, more than any one else in the jungle, is apt to go mad. Then he forgets he was ever afraid of any one, and runs through the forest biting everything in his way. Even the tiger runs and hides when little Tabaqui goes mad, for madness is the most disgraceful thing that can overtake a

wild creature. We call it hydrophobia, but they call it *dewanee*—the madness—and run.

"Enter, then, and look," said Father Wolf, stiffly, "but there is no food here."

"For a wolf, no," said Tabaqui; "but for so mean a person as myself a dry bone is a good feast. Who are we, the jackal people, to pick and choose?" He scuttled to the back of the cave, where he found the bone of a buck with some meat on it, and sat cracking the end merrily.

"All thanks for this good meal," he said, licking his lips. "How beautiful are your noble children! How large are their eyes! And so young too! Indeed, I might have remembered that the children of kings are men from the beginning."

Now, Tabaqui knew as well as any one else that there is nothing so unlucky as to compliment children to their faces, and it pleased him to see Mother and Father Wolf look uncomfortable. Tabaqui sat still, rejoicing in the mischief that he had made, and then he said spitefully:

"Shere Khan, the Big One, has shifted his hunting grounds. He will hunt among these hills for the next moon, so he has told me."

Shere Khan was the tiger who lived near the Waingunga River, twenty miles away.

"He has no right!" Father Wolf began angrily—"By the Law of the Jungle he has no right to change his quarters without due warning. He will frighten every head of game within ten miles, and I—I have to kill for two, these days."

"His mother did not call him Lungri (the Lame) for nothing," said Mother Wolf quietly. "He has been lame in one foot from his birth. That is why he has only killed cattle. Now the villagers of the Waingunga are angry with him, and he has come here to make *our* villagers angry. They will scour the jungle for him and we and our children must run when they set the grass alight. Indeed," she spoke bitterly now, "we are very grateful to Shere Khan!"

"Shall I tell him of your gratitude?" said Tabaqui.

"Out!" snapped Father Wolf. "Out and hunt with thy master. Thou hast done harm enough for one night."

"I go," said Tabaqui, quietly. "Ye can hear Shere Khan below in the thickets. I might have saved myself the message."

Father Wolf listened, and below in the valley that ran down to a little river, he heard the dry, angry, snarly, singsong whine of a tiger who has caught nothing and does not care if all the jungle knows it.

"The fool!" said Father Wolf. "To begin a night's work with that noise! Does he think that our buck are like his fat Waingunga bullocks?"

"H'sh. It is neither bullock nor buck he hunts to-night," said Mother Wolf. "It is Man." The whine had changed to a sort of humming purr that seemed to come from every quarter of the compass. It was the noise that bewilders woodcutters and Gypsies sleeping in the open, and makes them run sometimes into the very mouth of the tiger.

"Man!" said Father Wolf, showing all his white teeth.

"Faugh! Are there not enough beetles and frogs in the ponds that he must eat Man, and on our ground too!"

The Law of the Jungle, which never orders anything without a reason, forbids every beast to eat Man except when he is killing to show his children how to kill, and then he must hunt outside the hunting-grounds of his pack or tribe. The real reason for this is that man-killing means, sooner or later, the arrival of white men on elephants, with guns, and hundreds of brown men with gongs and rockets and torches. Then everybody in the jungle suffers. The reason the beasts give among themselves is that Man is the weakest and most defenseless of all living things, and it is unsportsmanlike to touch him. They say too—and it is true—that maneaters become mangy, and lose their teeth.

The purr grew louder, and ended in the full-throated "Aaarh!" of the tiger's charge.

Then there was a howl—an untigerish howl—from Shere Khan. "He has missed," said Mother Wolf "What is it?"

Father Wolf ran out a few paces and heard Shere Khan muttering and mumbling savagely, as he tumbled about in the scrub.

"The fool has had no more sense than to jump at a woodcutters' camp-fire, and has burned his feet," said Father Wolf, with a grunt. "Tabaqui is with him."

"Something is coming up hill," said Mother Wolf, twitching one ear. "Get ready."

The bushes rustled a little in the thicket, and Father Wolf dropped with his haunches under him, ready for his leap. Then, if you had been watching, you would have seen the most wonderful thing in the world—the wolf checked in mid-spring. He made his bound before he saw what it was he was jumping at, and then he tried to stop himself. The result was that he shot up straight into the air for four or five feet, landing almost where he left ground.

"Man!" he snapped. "A man's cub. Look!"

Directly in front of him, holding on by a low branch, stood a naked brown baby who could just walk—as soft and as dimpled a little atom as ever came to a wolf's cave at night. He looked up into Father Wolf's face, and laughed.

"Is that a man's cub?" said Mother Wolf. "I have never seen one. Bring it here."

A Wolf accustomed to moving his own cubs can, if necessary, mouth an egg without breaking it, and though Father Wolf's jaws closed right on the child's back not a tooth even scratched the skin, as he laid it down among the cubs.

"How little! How naked, and—how bold!" said Mother Wolf, softly. The baby was pushing his way between the cubs to get close to the warm hide. "Ahai! He is taking his meal with the others. Now, was there ever a wolf that could boast of a man's cub among her children?"

"I have heard now and again of such a thing, but never in our Pack or in my time," said Father Wolf. "He is altogether without hair, and I could kill him with a touch of my foot. But see, he looks up and is not afraid."

The moonlight was blocked out of the mouth of the cave, for Shere Khan's great square head and shoulders were thrust into the entrance. Tabaqui, behind him, was squeaking: "My lord, my lord, it went in here!"

"Shere Khan does us great honor," said Father Wolf, but his eyes were very angry. "What does Shere Khan need?"

"My quarry. A man's cub went this way," said Shere Khan. "Its parents have run off. Give it to me."

Shere Khan had jumped at a woodcutters' campfire, as Father Wolf had said, and was furious from the pain of his burned feet. But Father Wolf knew that the mouth of the cave was too narrow for a tiger to come in by. Even where he was, Shere Khan's shoulders and fore paws were cramped for want of room.

"The Wolves are a free people," said Father Wolf. "They take orders from the Head of the Pack, and not from any striped cattle-killer. The man's cub is ours— to kill if we choose."

"Ye choose and ye do not choose! What talk is this of choosing? By the bull that I killed, am I to stand nosing into your dog's den for my fair dues? It is I, Shere Khan, who speak!"

The tiger's roar filled the cave with thunder. Mother Wolf shook herself clear of the cubs and sprang forward, her eyes, like two green moons in the darkness, facing the blazing eyes of Shere Khan.

"And it is I, Raksha, The Demon, who answer. The man's cub is mine! He shall not be killed. He shall live to run with the Pack and to hunt with the Pack; and in the end, look you, hunter of little naked cubs—frog-eater—fish-killer—he shall hunt *thee*! Now get hence, or back thou goest to thy mother, burned beast of the jungle, lamer than ever thou camest into the world! Go!"

Father Wolf looked on amazed. He had almost forgotten the days when he won Mother Wolf in fair fight from five other wolves, when she ran in the Pack and was not called The Demon for compliment's sake. Shere Khan might have faced Father Wolf, but he could not stand up against Mother Wolf, for he knew that where he was, she had all the advantage of the ground, and would fight to the death. So he backed out of the cave-mouth growling, and when he was clear he shouted:

"Each dog barks in his own yard! We will see what the Pack will say to this fostering of man-cubs. The cub is mine! He is mine! And to my teeth he will come in the end, O bushtailed thieves!"

Mother Wolf threw herself down panting among the cubs, and Father Wolf said to her gravely:

"Shere Khan speaks this much truth. The cub must be shown to the Pack. Wilt thou keep him, Mother?"

"Keep him!" she gasped. "He came naked, by night, alone and very hungry, yet he was not afraid! Look, he has pushed one of my babes to one side already. And that lame butcher would have killed him and would have run off to the Waingunga while the villagers here hunted through all our lairs in revenge! Keep him? Assuredly I will keep him. Lie still, little frog. O thou Mowgli—for Mowgli the Frog I will call thee—the time

will come when thou wilt hunt Shere Khan as he has hunted thee."

"But what will our Pack say?" said Father Wolf. "What will they say to a man-cub?"

The Law of the Jungle lays down very clearly that any wolf may, when he marries, withdraw from the Pack he belongs to, but as soon as his cubs are old enough to stand on their feet he must bring them to the Pack Council, which is generally held once a month at full moon, in order that the other wolves may identify them. After that inspection the cubs are free to run where they please, and until they have killed their first buck no excuse is accepted if a grown wolf of the Pack kills one of them. The punishment is death where the murderer can be found.

Father Wolf waited till his cubs could run a little, and

then on the night of the Pack Meeting took them and
Mowgli and Mother Wolf to the Council Rock—a hilltop
covered with stones and boulders where a hundred
wolves could hide. Akela, the great gray Lone Wolf, who
led all the Pack by strength and cunning, lay out at full
length on his rock, and below him sat forty or more
wolves of every size and color, from badger-colored
veterans who could handle a buck alone, to young black
three-year-olds who thought they could. The Lone Wolf
had led them for a year now. He had fallen twice into a
wolftrap in his youth, and once he had been beaten and
left for dead, so he knew the manners and customs of
men. There was very little talking at the rock. The cubs
tumbled over each other in the center of the circle where
their mothers and fathers sat, and now and again a
senior wolf would go quietly up to a cub, look at him
carefully, and return to his place on noiseless feet.
Sometimes a mother would push her cub far out into
the moonlight, to be sure that he had not been overlooked. Akela from his rock would cry:

"Ye know the Law, ye know the Law. Look well,
O Wolves!"

And the anxious mothers would take up the call:
"Look! Look well, O Wolves."

At last—and Mother Wolf's neck-bristles lifted as the
time came—Father Wolf pushed "Mowgli the Frog," as
they called him, into the center, where he sat laughing
and playing with some pebbles that glistened in the
moonlight.

Akela never raised his head from his paws, but went

on with the monotonous cry: "Look well!" A muffled roar came from behind the rocks—the voice of Shere Khan crying: "The cub is mine. Give him to me. What have the Free People to do with a man's cub?" Akela never even twitched his ears, all he said was: "Look well, O Wolves! What have the Free People to do with the orders of any save the Free People? Look well!"

There was a chorus of deep growls, and a young wolf in his fourth year flung back Shere Khan's question to Akela: "What have the Free People to do with a man's cub? Now the Law of the Jungle lays down that if there is any dispute as to the right of a cub to be accepted by the Pack, he must be spoken for by at least two members of the Pack who are not his father and mother."

"Who speaks for this cub?" said Akela. "Among the Free People who speaks?" There was no answer, and Mother Wolf got ready for what she knew would be her last fight, if things came to fighting.

Then the only other creature who is allowed at the Pack Council—Baloo, the sleepy brown bear who teaches the wolf cubs the Law of the Jungle and can come and go where he pleases because he eats only nuts and roots and honey—old Baloo rose up on his hind quarters and grunted.

"The man's cub—the man's cub?" he said. "I speak for the man's cub. There is no harm in a man's cub. I have no gift of words, but I speak the truth. Let him run with the Pack, and be entered with the others. I myself will teach him."

"We need yet another," said Akela. "Baloo has

spoken, and he is our teacher for the young cubs. Who speaks beside Baloo?"

A black shadow dropped down into the circle, It was Bagheera the Black Panther, inky black all over, but with the panther markings showing up in certain lights like the patterns of watered silk. Everybody knew Bagheera, and nobody cared to cross his path, for he was as cunning as Tabaqui, as bold as the wild buffalo, and as reckless as the wounded elephant. But he had a voice as soft as wild honey dripping from a tree, and a skin softer than down.

"O Akela, and ye the Free People," he purred. I have no right in your assembly, but the Law of the Jungle says that if there is a doubt which is not a killing matter in regard to a new cub, the life of that cub may be bought at a price. And the Law does not say who may or may not pay that price. Am I right?"

"Good! Good!" said the young wolves, who are always hungry. "Listen to Bagheera. The cub can be bought for a price. It is the Law."

"Knowing that I have no right to speak here, I ask your leave."

"Speak then," cried twenty voices.

"To kill a naked cub is shame. Besides, he may make better sport for you when he is grown. Baloo has spoken in his behalf. Now to Baloo's word I will add one bull, a fat one, newly killed, if ye will accept the man's cub according to the Law."

There was a clamor of scores of voices, saying: "What matter? He will die in the winter rains. He will scorch in the sun. What harm can a naked frog do us? Let him run with the Pack. Where is the bull, Bagheera? Let him be accepted." And then came Akela's deep bay, crying: "Look well—look well, O Wolves!"

Mowgli was still deeply interested in the pebbles, and he did not notice when the wolves came and looked at him one by one. At last they all went down the hill for the dead bull, and only Akela, Bagheera, Baloo, and Mowgli's own wolves were left. Shere Khan roared still in the night, for he was very angry that Mowgli had not been handed over to him.

"Ay, roar well," said Bagheera, under his whiskers; "for the time comes when this naked thing will make thee roar to another tune, or I know nothing of man."

"It was well done," said Akela. "Men and their cubs are very wise. He may be a help in time."

"Truly, a help in time of need; for none can hope to lead the Pack forever," said Bagheera.

Akela said nothing. He was thinking of the time that comes to every leader of every pack when his strength goes from him and he gets feebler and feebler, till at last he is killed by the wolves and a new leader comes up—to be killed in his turn.

"Take him away," he said to Father Wolf, "and train him as befits one of the Free People."

Now you must be content to skip ten or eleven whole years, and only guess at all the wonderful life that Mowgli led among the wolves, because if it were written out it would fill ever so many books. He grew up with

the cubs, though they, of course, were grown wolves almost before he was a child, and Father Wolf taught him his business, and the meaning of things in the jungle till every rustle in the grass, every breath of the warm night air, every note of the owls above his head, every scratch of a bat's claws as it roosted for a while in a tree, and every splash of every little fish jumping in a pool, meant just as much to him as the work of his office means to a business man. When he was not learning he sat out in the sun and slept, and ate and went to sleep again; when he felt dirty or hot he swam in the forest pools; and when he wanted honey (Baloo told him that honey and nuts were just as pleasant to eat as raw meat) he climbed up for it, and that Bagheera showed him how to do. Bagheera would lie out on a branch and call, "Come along, Little Brother," and at first Mowgli would cling like the sloth, but afterward he would fling himself through the branches almost as boldly as the gray ape. He took his place at the Council Rock, too, when the Pack met, and there he discovered that if he stared hard at any wolf, the wolf would be forced to drop his eyes, and so he used to stare for fun. At other times he would pick the long thorns out of the pads of his friends, for wolves suffer terribly from thorns and burs in their coats. He would go down the hillside into the cultivated lands by night, and look very curiously at the villagers in their huts, but he had mistrust of men because Bagheera showed him a square box with a drop-gate so cunningly hidden in the jungle that he nearly walked into it, and told him that it was a trap. He loved better than anything else to go with Bagheera into the dark warm heart of the forest, to sleep all through the drowsy day, and at night see how Bagheera did his killing. Bagheera killed as he felt hungry, and so did Mowgli—with one exception. As soon as he was old enough to understand things, Bagheera told him that he must never touch cattle because he had been bought into the Pack at the price of a bull's life. "All the jungle is thine," said Bagheera, "and thou canst kill for thy food everything that thou art strong enough to kill; but for the sake of the bull that bought thee thou must never kill or eat any cattle young or old. That is the Law of the Jungle." Mowgli obeyed faithfully.

And he grew and grew strong as a boy must grow who does not know that he is learning any lessons, and who has nothing in the world to think of except things to eat.

Mother Wolf told him once or twice that Shere Khan was not a creature to be trusted, and that some day he must kill Shere Khan; but though a young wolf would have remembered that advice every hour, Mowgli forgot it because he was only a boy—though he would have called himself a wolf if he had been able to speak in any human tongue.

Shere Khan was always crossing his path in the jungle, for as Akela grew older and feebler the lame tiger had come to be great friends with the younger wolves of the Pack, who followed him for scraps, a thing Akela would never have allowed if he had dared to push his authority to the proper bounds. Then Shere Khan would flatter them and wonder that such fine young hunters were content to be led by a dying wolf and a man's cub. "They tell me," Shere Khan would say, "that at Council ye dare not look him between the eyes"; and the young wolves would growl and bristle.

Bagheera, who had eyes and ears everywhere, knew something of this, and once or twice he told Mowgli in so many words that Shere Khan would kill him some day; and Mowgli would laugh and answer: "I have the Pack and I have thee. And Baloo, though he is so lazy, might strike a blow or two for my sake. Why should I be afraid?"

It was one very warm day that a new notion came to Bagheera—born of something that he had heard. Perhaps Sahi the Porcupine had told him; but he said to Mowgli when they were deep in the jungle, as the boy lay with his head on Bagheera's beautiful black skin:

"Little Brother, how often have I told thee that Shere Khan is thy enemy?"

"As many times as there are nuts on that palm," said Mowgli, who naturally, could not count. "What of it? I am sleepy, Bagheera, and Shere Khan is all long tail and loud talk—like Mor the Peacock."

"But this is no time for sleeping. Baloo knows it; I know it; the Pack know it; and even the foolish, foolish deer know. Tabaqui has told thee, too."

"Ho! ho!" said Mowgli. "Tabaqui came to me not long ago with some rude talk that I was a naked man's cub and not fit to dig pig-nuts; but I caught Tabaqui by the tail and swung him twice against a palm-tree to teach him better manners."

"That was foolishness; for though Tabaqui is a mischiefmaker, he would have told thee of something that concerned thee closely. Open those eyes, Little Brother. Shere Khan dare not kill thee in the jungle; but remember, Akela is very old, and soon the day comes when he cannot kill his buck, and then he will be leader no more. Many of the wolves that looked thee over when thou wast brought to the Council first are old too, and the young wolves believe, as Shere Khan has taught them, that a man-cub has no place with the Pack. In a little time thou wilt be a man."

"And what is a man that he should not run with his brothers?" said Mowgli. "I was born in the jungle. I have obeyed the Laws of the Jungle, and there is no wolf of ours from whose paws I have not pulled a thorn. Surely they are my brothers!"

Bagheera stretched himself at full length and half shut his eyes. "Little Brother," said he, "feel under my jaw."

Mowgli put up his strong brown hand, and just under Bagheera's silky chin, where the giant rolling muscles were all hid by the glossy hair, he came upon a little bald spot.

"There is no one in the jungle that knows that I, Bagheera, carry that mark—the mark of the collar; and yet, Little Brother, I was born among men, and it was among men that my mother died—in the cages of the King's Palace at Oodeypore. It was because of this that I paid the price for thee at the Council when thou wast a little naked cub. Yes, I, too, was born among men. I had never seen the jungle. They fed me behind bars from an iron pan till one night I felt that I was Bagheera —the Panther—and no man's plaything, and I broke the silly lock with one blow of my paw and came away. And because I had learned the ways of men, I became more terrible in the jungle than Shere Khan. Is it not so?"

"Yes," said Mowgli, "all the jungle fear Bagheera— all except Mowgli."

"Oh, *thou* art a man's cub," said the Black Panther, very tenderly, "and even as I returned to my jungle, so thou must go back to men at last—to the men who are thy brothers—if thou art not killed in the Council."

"But why—but why should any wish to kill me?" said Mowgli.

"Look at me," said Bagheera; and Mowgli looked at

him steadily between the eyes. The big panther turned his head away in half a minute.

"*That* is why," he said, shifting his paw on the leaves. "Not even I can look thee between the eyes, and I was born among men, and I love thee, Little Brother. The others, they hate thee because their eyes cannot meet thine; because thou art wise; because thou has pulled out thorns from their feet—because thou art a man."

"I did not know these things," said Mowgli, sullenly, and he frowned under his heavy black eyebrows.

"What is the Law of the Jungle? Strike first and then give tongue. By thy very carelessness they know that thou art a man. But be wise. It is in my heart that when Akela misses his next kill—and at each hunt it costs him more to pin the buck—the Pack will turn against him and against thee. They will hold a jungle Council at the Rock, and then—and then—I have it!" said Bagheera, leaping up. "Go thou down quickly to the men's huts in the valley, and take some of the Red Flower which they grow there, so that when the time comes thou mayest have even a stronger friend than I or Baloo or those of the Pack that love thee. Get the Red Flower." By Red Flower Bagheera meant fire, only no creature in the jungle will call fire by its proper name. Every beast lives in deadly fear of it, and invents a hundred ways of describing it.

"The Red Flower?" said Mowgli. "That grows outside their huts in the twilight. I will get some."

"There speaks the man's cub," said Bagheera, proudly. "Remember that it grows in little pots. Get one swiftly, and keep it by thee for time of need."

"Good!" said Mowgli. "I go. But art thou sure, O my Bagheera"—he slipped his arm around the splendid neck, and looked deep into the big eyes—"art thou sure that all this is Shere Khan's doing?"

"By the Broken Lock that freed me, I am sure, Little Brother."

"Then, by the Bull that bought me, I will pay Shere Khan full tale for this, and it may be a little over," said Mowgli; and he bounded away.

"That is a man. He is all a man," said Bagheera to himself, lying down again. "Oh, Shere Khan, never was a blacker hunting than that frog-hunt of thine ten years ago!"

Mowgli was far and far through the forest, running hard, and his heart was hot in him. He came to the cave as the evening mist rose, and drew breath, and looked down the valley. The cubs were out, but Mother Wolf, at the back of the cave, knew by his breathing that something was troubling her frog.

"What is it, Son?" she said.

"Some bat's chatter of Shere Khan," he called back. "I hunt among the ploughed fields to-night"; and he plunged downward through the bushes, to the stream at the bottom of the valley. There he checked, for he heard the yell of the Pack hunting, heard the bellow of a hunted buck, and the snort as the buck turned at bay. Then there were wicked, bitter howls from the young wolves: "Akela! Akela! Let the Lone Wolf show his strength. Room for the leader of the Pack! Spring,

Akela!"

The Lone Wolf must have sprung and missed his hold, for Mowgli heard the snap of his teeth and then a yelp as the buck knocked him over with his fore foot.

He did not wait for anything more, but dashed on; and the yells grew fainter behind him as he ran into the croplands where the villagers lived.

"Bagheera spoke truth," he panted, as he nestled down in some cattle-fodder by the window of a hut. "Tomorrow is one day both for Akela and for me."

Then he pressed his face close to the window and watched the fire on the hearth. He saw the husband man's wife get up and feed it in the night with black lumps; and when the morning came and the mists were all white and cold, he saw the man's child pick up a wicker pot plastered inside with earth, fill it with lumps of red-hot charcoal, put it under his blanket, and go out to tend the cows in the cow barn.

"Is that all?" said Mowgli. "If a cub can do it, there is nothing to fear." So he strode round the corner and met the boy, took the pot from his hand, and disappeared into the mist while the boy howled with fear.

"They are very like me," said Mowgli, blowing into the pot, as he had seen the woman do. "This thing will die if I do not give it things to eat"; and he dropped twigs and dried bark on the red stuff. Half-way up the hill he met Bagheera with the morning dew shining like moonstones on his coat.

"Akela has missed," said the Panther. "They would have killed him last night, but they needed thee also.

They were looking for thee on the hill."

"I was among the ploughed lands. I am ready. See!" Mowgli held up the fire-pot.

"Good!" said Bagheera. "I have seen men thrust a dry branch into that stuff, and presently the Red Flower blossomed at the end of it. Art thou not afraid?"

"No. Why should I fear?" Mowgli answered. "I remember now—if it is not a dream—how, before I was a Wolf, I lay beside the Red Flower, and it was warm and pleasant."

All that day Mowgli sat in the cave tending his fire-pot and dipping dry branches into it to see how they looked. He found a branch that satisfied him, and in the evening when Tabaqui came to the cave and told him rudely that he was wanted at the Council Rock, he laughed till Tabaqui ran away. Then Mowgli went to the Council, still laughing.

Akela the Lone Wolf lay by the side of his rock as a sign that the leadership of the Pack was open, and Shere Khan with his following of scrap-fed wolves walked to and fro, openly being flattered. Bagheera lay close to Mowgli, and the fire-pot was between Mowgli's knees. When they were all gathered together, Shere Khan began to speak—a thing he would never have dared to do when Akela was in his prime.

"He has no right," whispered Bagheera. "Say so. He is a dog's son. He will be frightened."

Mowgli sprang to his feet. "Free People," he cried, "does Shere Khan lead the Pack? What has a tiger to do with our leadership?"

"Seeing that the leadership is yet open, and being asked to speak—" Shere Khan began.

"By whom?" said Mowgli. "Are we *all* jackals, to fawn on this cattle-butcher? The leadership of the Pack is with the Pack alone."

There were yells of "Silence, thou man's cub! Let him speak. He has kept our Law"; and at last the seniors of the Pack thundered: "Let the Dead Wolf speak." When a leader of the Pack has missed his kill, he is called the Dead Wolf as long as he lives, which is not long.

Akela raised his old head wearily.

"Free People," he said, "and ye, too, jackals of Shere Khan, for twelve seasons I have led ye to and from the kill, and in all that time not one of you has been trapped or maimed. Now I have missed my kill. Ye know how that plot was made. Ye know how ye brought me up to an untried buck to make my weakness known. It was cleverly done. Your right is to kill me here on the Council Rock, now. Therefore, I ask, who comes to make an end of the Lone Wolf? For it is my right, by the Law of the Jungle, that ye come one by one."

There was a long hush, for no single wolf cared to fight Akela to the death. Then Shere Khan roared: "Bah! What have we to do with this toothless fool? He is doomed to die! It is the man-cub who has lived too long. Free People, he was my meat from the first. Give him to me. I am weary of this man-wolf folly. He has troubled the jungle for ten seasons. Give me the man-cub, or I will hunt here always, and not give you one bone. He is a man, a man's child, and from the marrow of my bones

I hate him!"

Then more than half the Pack yelled: "A man! A man! What has a man to do with us? Let him go to his own place."

"And turn all the people of the villagers against us?" clamored Shere Khan. "No, give him to me. He is a man, and none of us can look him between the eyes."

Akela lifted his head again, and said: "He has eaten our food. He has slept with us. He has driven game for us. He has broken no word of the Law of the Jungle."

"Also, I paid for him with a bull when he was accepted. The worth of a bull is little, but Bagheera's honor is something that he will perhaps fight for," said Bagheera, in his gentlest voice.

"A bull paid ten years ago!" the Pack snarled. "What do we care for bones ten years old?"

"Or for a pledge?" said Bagheera, his white teeth bared under his lip. "Well are ye called the Free People!"

"No man's cub can run with the people of the jungle," howled Shere Khan. "Give him to me!"

"He is our brother in all but blood," Akela went on; "and ye would kill him here! In truth, I have lived too long. Some of ye are eaters of cattle, and of others I have heard that, under Shere Khan's teaching, ye go by dark night and snatch children from the villager's doorstep. Therefore I know ye to be cowards, and it is to cowards I speak. It is certain that I must die, and my life is of no worth, or I would offer that in the man-cub's place. But for the sake of the Honor of the Pack—a little matter that ye have forgotten—I promise that if ye let the man-cub go to his own place, I will not, when my time comes to die, bare one tooth against ye. I will die without fighting. That will at least save the Pack three lives. More I cannot do; but if ye will, I can save ye the shame that comes of killing a brother against whom there is no fault—a brother spoken for and bought into the Pack according to the Law of the Jungle."

"He is a man—a man—a man!" snarled the Pack; and most of the wolves began to gather round Shere Khan, whose tail was beginning to switch.

"Now the business is in thy hands," said Bagheera to Mowgli. "We can do no more except fight."

Mowgli stood upright—the fire-pot in his hands. Then he stretched out his arms, and yawned in the face of the Council; but he was furious with rage and sorrow, for, wolf-like, the wolves had never told him how they hated him. "Listen you!" he cried. "There is no need for this dog's jabber. Ye have told me I am a man so often to-night, that, though I would have been a wolf with you to my life's end, I now feel your words are true. So I do not call ye my brothers any more, but dogs, as a man should. What ye will do, and what ye will not do, is not yours to say. That matter is with *me*; and that we may see the matter more plainly, I, the man, have brought here a little of the Red Flower which ye, dogs, fear."

He flung the fire-pot on the ground, and some of the red coals lit a tuft of dried moss that flared up, as all the Council drew back in terror before the leaping flames.

Mowgli thrust his dead branch into the fire till the

twigs lit and crackled, and whirled it above his head among the cowering wolves.

"Thou art the master," said Bagheera, in an undertone. "Save Akela from the death. He was ever thy friend."

Akela, the grim old wolf who had never asked for mercy in his life, gave one piteous look at Mowgli as the boy stood all naked, his long black hair tossing over his shoulders in the light of the blazing branch that made the shadows jump and quiver.

"Good!" said Mowgli, staring round slowly. "I see that ye are dogs. I go from you to my own people—if they be my own people. The Jungle is shut to me, and I must forget your talk and your companionship; but I will be more merciful than ye are. Because I was all but your brother in blood, I promise that when I am a man among men I will not betray ye to men as ye have betrayed me." He kicked the fire with his foot, and the sparks flew up. "There shall be no war between any of us in the Pack. But here is a debt to pay before I go." He strode forward to where Shere Khan sat blinking stupidly at the flames, and caught him by the tuft on his chin. Bagheera followed in case of accidents. "Up, dog!" Mowgli cried. "Up, when a man speaks, or I will set that coat ablaze!"

Shere Khan's ears lay flat back on his head, and he shut his eyes, for the blazing branch was very near.

"This cattle-killer said he would kill me in the Council because he had not killed me when I was a cub. Thus and thus, then, do we beat dogs when we are men. Stir a whisker, Lame-One, and I ram the Red Flower down thy gullet!" He beat Shere Khan over the head with the branch, and the tiger whimpered and whined in an agony of fear.

"Pah! Singed jungle-cat—go now! But remember when next I come to the Council Rock, as a man should come, it will be with Shere Khan's hide on my head. For the rest, Akela goes free to live as he pleases. Ye will *not* kill him, because that is not my will. Nor do I think that ye will sit here any longer, lolling out your tongues as though ye were somebodies, instead of dogs whom I drive out—thus! Go!" The fire was burning furiously at the end of the branch, and Mowgli struck right and left round the circle, and the wolves ran howling with the sparks burning their fur. At last there were only Akela, Bagheera, and perhaps ten wolves that had taken Mowgli's part. Then something began to hurt Mowgli inside him, as he had never been hurt in his life before, and he caught his breath and sobbed, and the tears ran down his face.

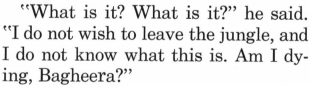

"What is it? What is it?" he said. "I do not wish to leave the jungle, and I do not know what this is. Am I dying, Bagheera?"

"No, Little Brother. That is only tears such as men use," said Bagheera. "Now I know thou art a man, and a man's cub no longer. The Jungle is shut indeed to thee henceforward. Let them fall, Mowgli. They are only tears." So Mowgli sat and cried as though his heart would break; and he had never cried in all his life before.

"Now," he said, "I will go to men. But first I must say farewell to my mother;" and he went to the cave where she lived with Father Wolf, and he cried on her coat, while the four cubs howled miserably.

"Ye will not forget me?" said Mowgli.

"Never while we can follow a trail," said the cubs. "Come to the foot of the hill when thou art a man, and we will talk to thee; and we will come into the crop-lands to play with thee by night."

"Come soon!" said Father Wolf. "Oh, wise little frog, come again soon; for we be old, thy mother and I."

"Come soon," said Mother Wolf, "little naked son of mine; for, listen, child of man, I loved thee more than ever I loved my cubs."

"I will surely come," said Mowgli; "and when I come it will be to lay Shere Khan's hide on the Council Rock. Do not forget me! Tell them in the jungle never to forget me!"

The dawn was beginning to break when Mowgli went down the hillside alone, to meet those mysterious things that are called men.

Freddy, the Pad Dog*
F. BEVERLY KELLEY

FREDDY was the smartest dog in the whole circus. There were other smart dogs, of course, for this was the biggest circus in the world. There was the little fox terrier that climbed to the top of a tall ladder and then jumped into a net. There were the collie dogs that rode bareback on pretty little Shetland ponies as they galloped around the tanbark-covered ring. There were sleek greyhounds that leaped over high hurdles, and there were the snow-white shepherd dogs that balanced themselves on the heads of wise old elephants in the grand entry.

But Freddy was the smartest dog of all. Freddy was a Boston bull, although it should be explained that he was much more than that. Freddy was what the circus calls

*Mr. Kelley once served as publicity director for Ringling Brothers and Barnum & Bailey Circus, and the story of *Freddy, the Pad Dog*, is based on a true incident. Copyright 1942 by Story Parade Inc. Reprinted by permission.

a "pad dog." A pad dog is taught to chase a clown and grab between his teeth a pad which is hidden in the seat of the clown's big flapping pants. Every afternoon and every evening, rain or shine, for nearly seven months while the circus traveled all over the country, Freddy could be seen with Shorty and dozens of other clowns who cut capers on the hippodrome track.

At one point in the performance, Shorty, who dressed like a comic policeman, would pretend to get into a fight with another clown named Mickey. Freddy would bark loudly while this was going on and then, when the clown policeman had hit Mickey several times with a soft club, Freddy would pretend to be very mad and would chase Shorty around the tent. When they were directly in front of the grandstand, Freddy would leap at the clown cop and sink his teeth into the pad worn in the seat of the clown's trousers. Then Shorty would yell at the top of his lungs and keep right on going until he was outside the tent, and all the time Freddy would be hanging on.

People laughed harder at Freddy and the clown policeman than they did at anything else in the show.

Back in the dressing tent, Shorty and Freddy were great pals. In fact, all the circus performers liked Freddy and most of them agreed that he was the smartest dog in the troupe. And yet, they had to admit that Freddy had one very serious fault.

It was serious because sometimes it spoiled the act. Every once in a while, Freddy would forget to keep his mind on the business at hand. When he was supposed to be chasing the clown around the tent, he would stop for a visit with almost anyone who would whistle at him and offer him candy or crackerjack. At times like this, Shorty would run all the way around the hippodrome oval and out through the performers' exit—and Freddy wouldn't be following him. Freddy would be having a grand time eating crackerjack with some stranger.

And so, although they were very fond of Freddy, the circus people felt that the way he left his work to become friendly with strangers was no way for a real trouper to act. One day the circus manager called Shorty into his big red office wagon and told him that if Freddy didn't behave, he would be taken out of the show.

This made the clown feel bad and he told the dog what the manager had said. Freddy was very quiet while Shorty was talking to him and it seemed that he understood. That very evening, however, when Freddy was chasing the clown, a boy whistled to him and Freddy stopped right in his tracks. Instead of leaping at the clown policeman and grabbing the pad in his teeth, Freddy calmly trotted into the grandstand where the boy sat and greedily ate the candy that the boy offered to him. This made some of the spectators laugh, but not nearly so much as they would have laughed at Shorty with Freddy hanging onto his funny blue pants.

Later that night, when the dog wagon in which Freddy rode with the other canine actors was rolled onto the long, flat railroad cars, Freddy was just as cheerful as you please. Freddy didn't know that at that very moment the circus manager had sent the equestrian director to tell Shorty the bad news about Freddy.

Next day, the circus pitched its billowing big-top in another town and when, at a quarter to two in the afternoon, the dogs were taken from their corral to be made ready for the grand entry, Freddy was left in his compartment. He couldn't understand it at all. The only time that dogs were left in their pens during the whole performance was when they were sick, and Freddy certainly wasn't sick. He never had felt better in his life.

Then one of the bandsmen blew a bugle call to warn all the circus people that they must line up for the opening parade. And at last Freddy heard the shrill blast of the equestrian director's whistle which started the procession moving into the big-top. The band played a lively air, and spangles flashed in the sun as the procession moved into the tent, around the hippodrome track and out again. And all the time Freddy was jumping at the door of his wire pen and barking as if to say,

"Let me out! I belong in the grand entry! You can't put on the show without me!" But nobody paid attention.

After the opening procession was finished and the performance had begun in earnest, Freddy forgot that he had been overlooked and stretched out on the clean shavings in his pen to wait for Shorty, who always came for him a few minutes before their clown act. Time came for the act, but no Shorty. This worried Freddy and he stood with his nose against the wire pen, watching the clowns hurry in and out of the big-top. Soon the clown routine, in which Freddy and the clown policeman always took part, was finished and Freddy hadn't even been out of his pen. This was indeed a puzzle to Freddy.

At last he spied Shorty walking toward him. But Shorty had on his street clothes instead of the funny uniform he wore when he was a clown cop. He took the dog up in his arms and said, "It looks as if you and I are quits, pal. The boss gave you one last chance to behave yourself and you just wouldn't do it. He says he is going to take you home for the winter when the show closes, and that he will give you to his little boy who wants a dog. Looks as if the trouping days are over, Freddy."

Now Freddy didn't understand all that Shorty said, but he did know that something was wrong. The clown wiped a tear from his eye, and Shorty never cried unless he felt very, very sad. So Freddy just licked the clown's hand and snuggled against his coat.

Every day during the rest of the time the circus was on tour that autumn, Shorty came to the dog corral to see Freddy. But they never went into the big tent together any more where they had made so many people hold their sides with laughter while the little clown policeman raced down the track with Freddy holding onto the seat of his pants.

At last the circus went into winter quarters and Freddy became the property of Peter, the circus manager's little boy. They were fast friends and romped from morning till night. At bedtime, Freddy stretched out on a rug in a corner of the kitchen.

During that winter, Freddy almost forgot that he ever had been a circus dog. But one day, just before the big show was to leave for the road tour, the circus manager took his little son and Freddy with him on a visit to winter quarters. Red-and-gold wagons were being painted and new tents made and animals trained in preparation for the new season. And when he trotted into one of the buildings, Freddy barked and wiggled with sheer delight because there was Shorty, the clown cop. Perhaps Shorty would practice their old tricks again.

Shorty was talking to the circus manager, "I've got a new pup to do that 'pad' act, Chief, but he isn't nearly as good at it as Freddy was."

And the manager replied, "I'm sorry, Shorty, but Freddy can't be trusted. He makes a fine playmate for Peter, but as a performer he is not dependable. You will have to do the best you can with the new dog."

Then Freddy nuzzled his snubby little nose into Shorty's arm and whimpered as though asking for one more chance. He would show them what a good trouper he could be. But neither Shorty nor the circus boss seemed to understand. When Freddy went home he was feeling worse than he ever had felt before.

That night, asleep in the kitchen, Freddy dreamed that he was with the circus again. He dreamed the band was playing and that flags were flying on the big tents and that hundreds of children were laughing at him as he chased Shorty around the hippodrome track.

Suddenly there was a noise that startled Freddy. It was quite dark in the kitchen, but Freddy could see dimly the form of a man hurrying through the door into the dining room. Not completely awake from his dream about chasing Shorty in the circus tent, Freddy was off like a shot and he leaped at the form in the darkness. The man yelled as the dog sank his teeth into his trouser seat and into flesh, and he tried to beat Freddy off with a club.

Freddy held on although he was beaten half unconscious, and in a few moments the room was flooded with light and the circus manager stood in the doorway with a revolver in his hand. "Put up your hands!" he said very sternly to the intruder. Then he smiled at Freddy and said;

"All right, old boy, you can let go now."

So Freddy let go and dropped onto the floor. He was hurt and very weak, and he couldn't remember very clearly just why he had grabbed the man, anyhow. It was all mixed up with the dream about Shorty, but this fellow didn't look like Shorty. Freddy gave it up—he ached all over and he was very tired.

Soon two men in blue uniforms came and took away the man Freddy had grabbed. Their uniforms resembled the clown policeman suit that Shorty wore in the circus, but these men didn't act like clowns at all. They were very gruff as they handcuffed their prisoner.

Then the circus manager and Peter, who was awake now and had come downstairs to see what the excitement was all about, bathed Freddy where he was hurt and covered him with a warm blanket. And the circus manager said, "Freddy, old timer, you made up for all your mistakes tonight because you caught a thief who broke in here to rob us. Do you know what I am going to do? I am going to see that you get back into the big show with Shorty again!"

Freddy wagged his tail and fell asleep to dream about the happy days to come.

HIAWATHA'S CHILDHOOD*
HENRY WADSWORTH LONGFELLOW

BY THE shores of Gitche Gúmee,
By the shining Big-Sea-Water,
Stood the wigwam of Nokómis.
Dark behind it rose the forest,
Rose the black and gloomy pine-trees,
Rose the firs with cones upon them;
Bright before it beat the water,
Beat the clear and sunny water,
Beat the shining Big-Sea-Water.

There the wrinkled, old Nokómis
Nursed the little Hiawátha,
Rocked him in his linden cradle,
Bedded soft in moss and rushes,
Stilled his fretful wail by saying,
"Hush! the Naked Bear will hear thee!"
Lulled him into slumber, singing.

*The cantata, *Hiawatha's Childhood*, by Bessie Whiteley presents, in the rhythm of Indian music, this lovely tale of the child, Hiawatha. Reprinted by permission of the publishers, Houghton Mifflin Company.

222

At the door on summer evenings
Sat the little Hiawátha,
Heard the whispering of the pine-trees,
Heard the lapping of the water,
   Saw the fire-fly, Wah-wah-tay'-see,
Flitting through the dusk of evening,
With the twinkle of its candle
Lighting up the brakes and bushes,
And he sang the song of children,
Sang the song Nokómis taught him:
"Wah-wah-tay'-see, little fire-fly,
Little, flitting, white-fire insect,
Little, dancing, white-fire creature,
Light me with your little candle,
Ere upon my bed I lay me,
Ere in sleep I close my eyelids!"
Saw the moon rise from the water,
Rippling, rounding from the water,

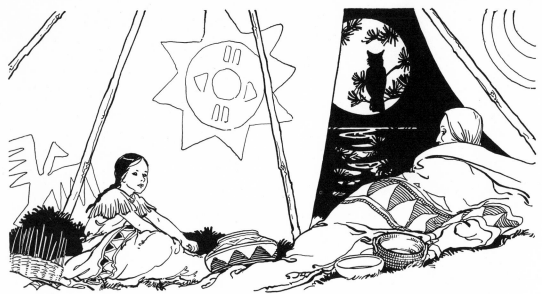

Saw the rainbow in the heaven,
In the eastern sky, the rainbow,
Whispered, "What is that, Nokómis?"
And the good Nokómis answered:
" 'Tis the heaven of flowers you see there;
All the wild-flowers of the forest,
All the lilies of the prairie,
When on earth they fade and perish,
Blossom in that heaven above us."
   When he heard the owls at midnight,
Hooting, laughing in the forest,
"What is that," he said, "Nokómis?"
And the good Nokómis answered:
"That is but the owl and owlet,
Talking in their native language,
Talking, scolding at each other."
   Then the little Hiawátha
Learned of every bird its language,
Learned their names and all their secrets,
How they built their nests in Summer,
Where they hid themselves in Winter,
Talked with them whene'er he met them,
Called them "Hiawátha's Chickens."